Helicopter Aerodynamics Made Simple

Well... relatively simple!

Geoff Day

First Edition

This book has been produced in A4 format with ring binding to aid its use as study material.

Published by Geoff Day

Printed in Great Britain by the MPG Books Group, Bodmin and King's Lynn

CONTENTS

FOREWORD

I am not an aerodynamicist. I am a pilot. Ever since I started flying on 13th August 1966 I've been trying to work out how the damn things fly - firstly with fixed wing - subsequently with helicopters. When, ten years later, I became a Flying Instructor, I had the task of explaining this to my students.

Helicopter Aerodynamics can easily get very complicated; there is, after all, a lot going on with blades that are whirling around at high speed. Over the years I have tried to get the explanations simple, basic and easy to understand. Of course, when doing this there is always the danger of making things too simple. Hopefully, I have been able to strike the right balance.

Sometimes I have taken examples to the extreme in order to illustrate a point. I have always tried to separate out various aerodynamic effects, whereas in reality they may merge due to the speed at which things happen.

If you are an aerodynamicist reading this book and you disagree with some of my explanations, then I apologise. However, if there is one pilot or potential pilot who finds that this book sheds some light on the "dark art" then I will be more than satisfied.

I am grateful to all the students that I have taught over the years for their feedback.

- Captain Geoff Day

Ok, so you're going to learn to fly a helicopter. Apart from the requirements to pass the helicopter technical examination, your own curiosity will probably prompt you to find out what makes a helicopter fly. Well, I'll try and explain - and keep it simple.

First of all, a bit of background. A guy called Bernoulli managed to prove, that in the steady streamline flow of an ideal fluid, the sum of the energies present remains a constant. Now don't worry, this is about as complicated as it gets. What this means in real language is that if you take a tube and blow air through it, what comes out will be the same as what went in.

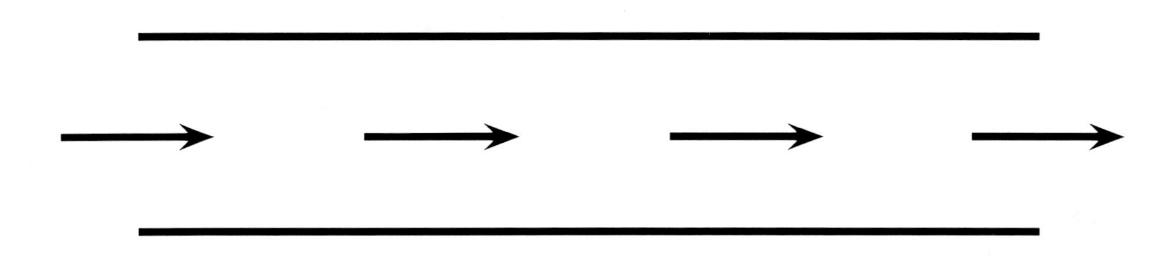

If we now put a restriction in the tube the air will have to speed up to get through; a bit like water in a river where it narrows.

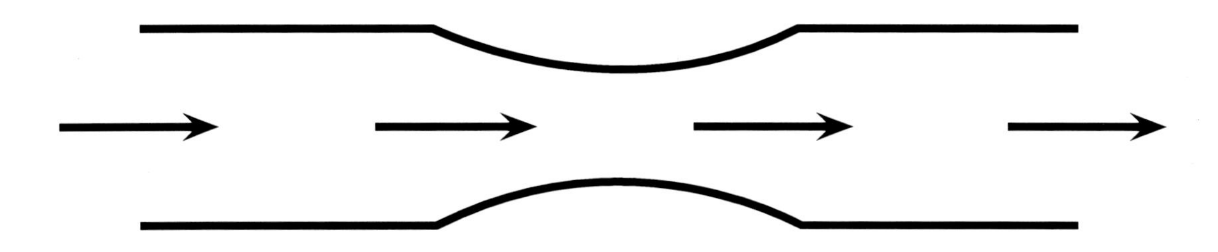

Now if the velocity (V) increases, then the pressure (P) reduces (just as that man Bernoulli suggested!).

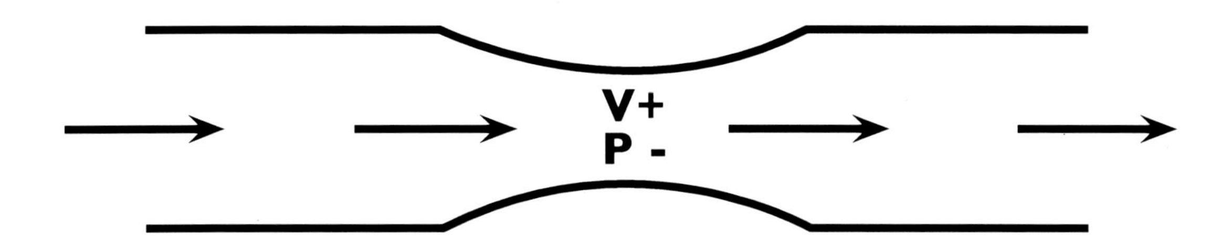

If we now take away the top part of the tube and just look at the bottom part then you will see that we almost have an aerofoil :

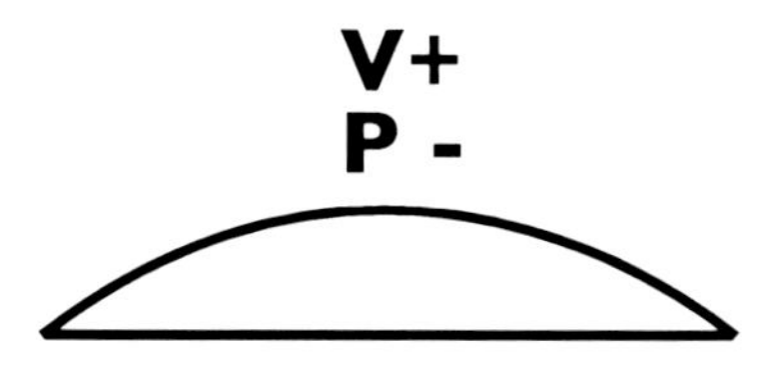

There is less pressure on top so the aerofoil will want to go up (Lift). Whenever Lift is generated, Drag is also produced, acting at 90° to the Lift.

Now don't be difficult. If I'm going to keep this simple, you'll have to accept this concept. We can generate more Lift from the aerofoil if we offer it at an angle to the air :

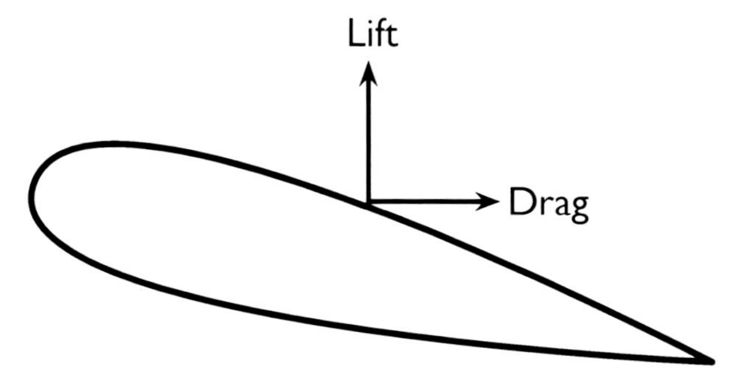

The air flowing over the aerofoil will be deflected downwards before rejoining the free stream airflow. If we put another aerofoil immediately behind the first, then the air which has been deflected downwards is deflected down even more.

Put enough aerofoils close enough together and the air which is flowing horizontally is induced to flow vertically, and hence is called induced flow. This is exactly what happens with the rotors on a helicopter :

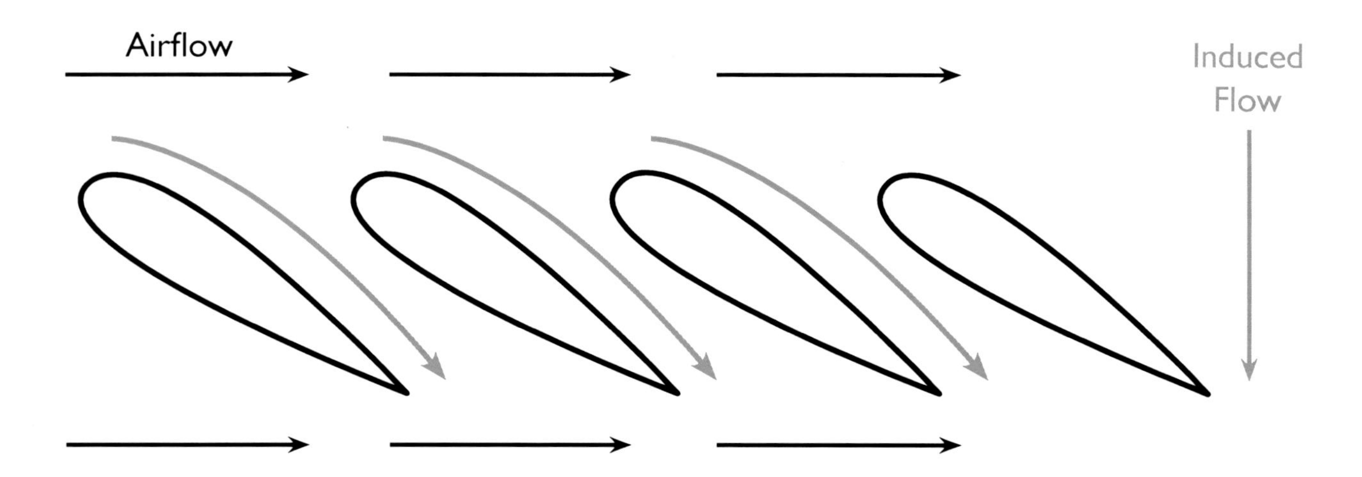

So far, so good I hope. Let's now look at what happens to an individual blade. We are going to construct a vector diagram, which is a stylised description of the forces acting on a blade at a particular moment in time.

Firstly take an aerofoil, a blade :

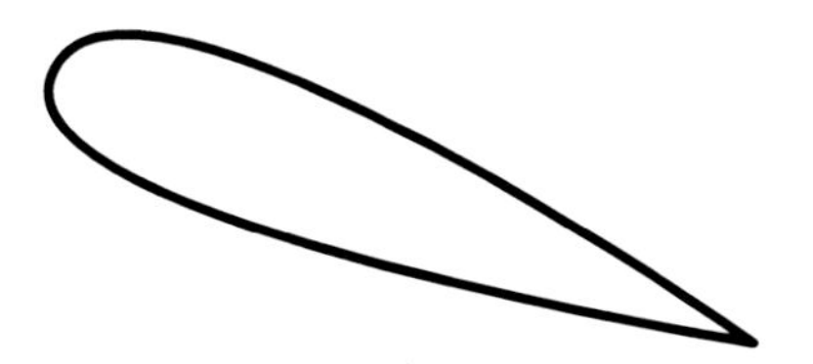

Let's have it turning - coming out of the page, going left to right into the page and then right to left.

It goes around an axis of rotation, in a plane of rotation.

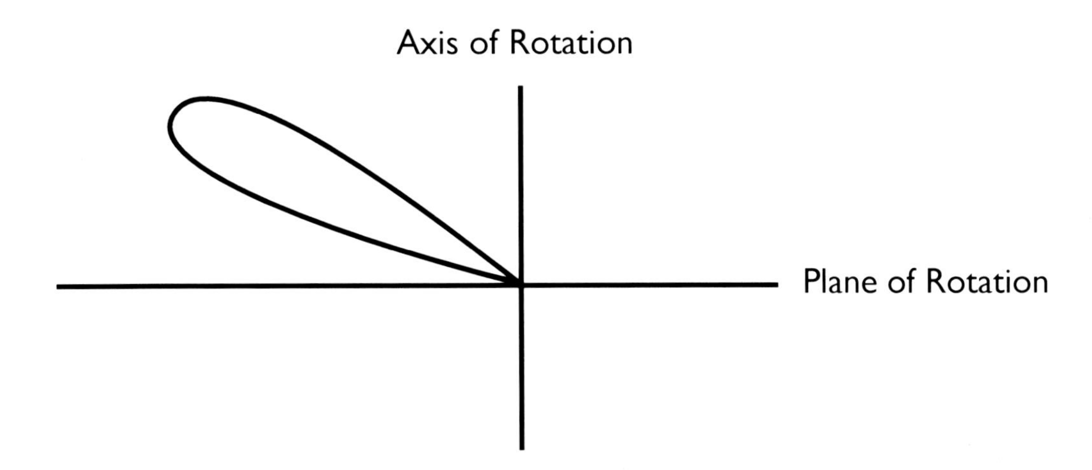

Because it is travelling through the air it has rotational flow, represented by a blue arrow (Vector) :

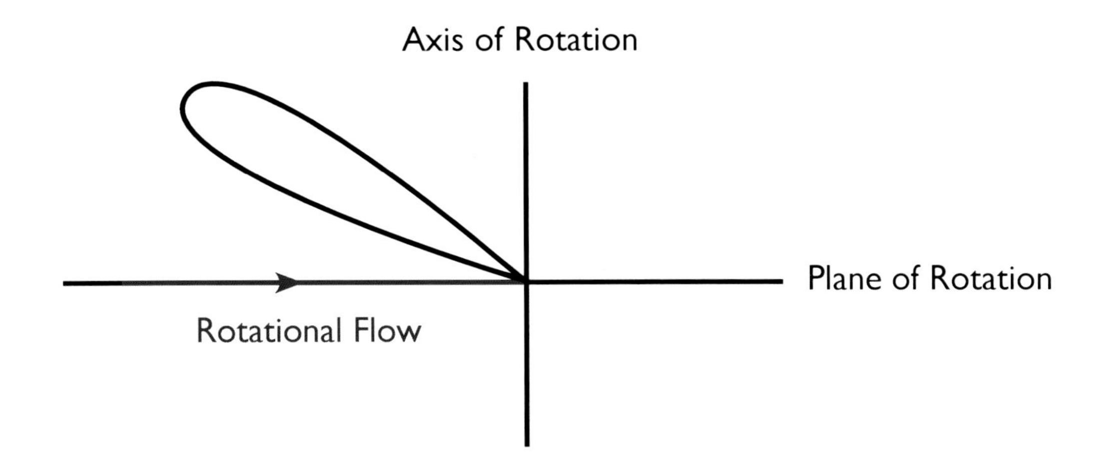

And we know that it has induced flow, represented by a green arrow :

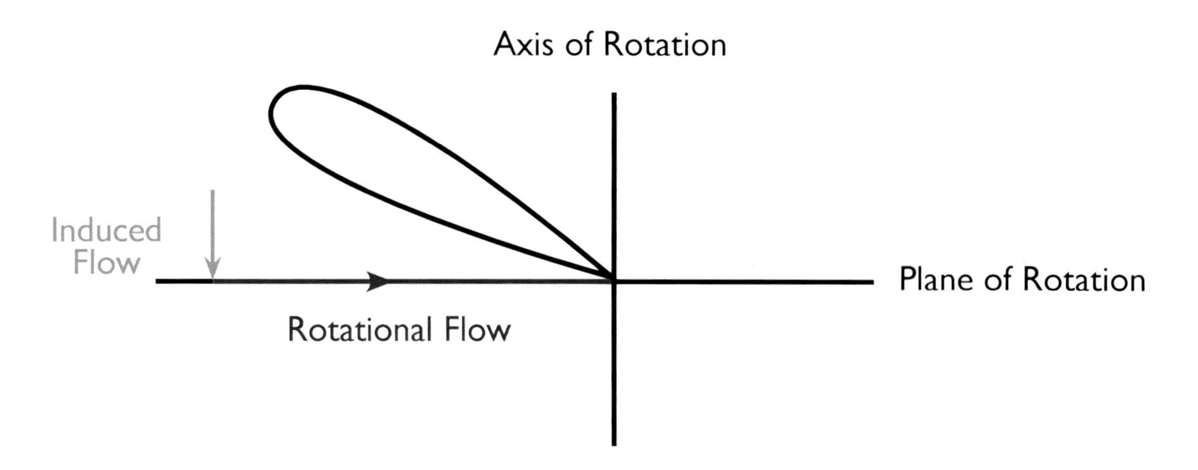

The resultant of these two is the relative air flow (RAF) :

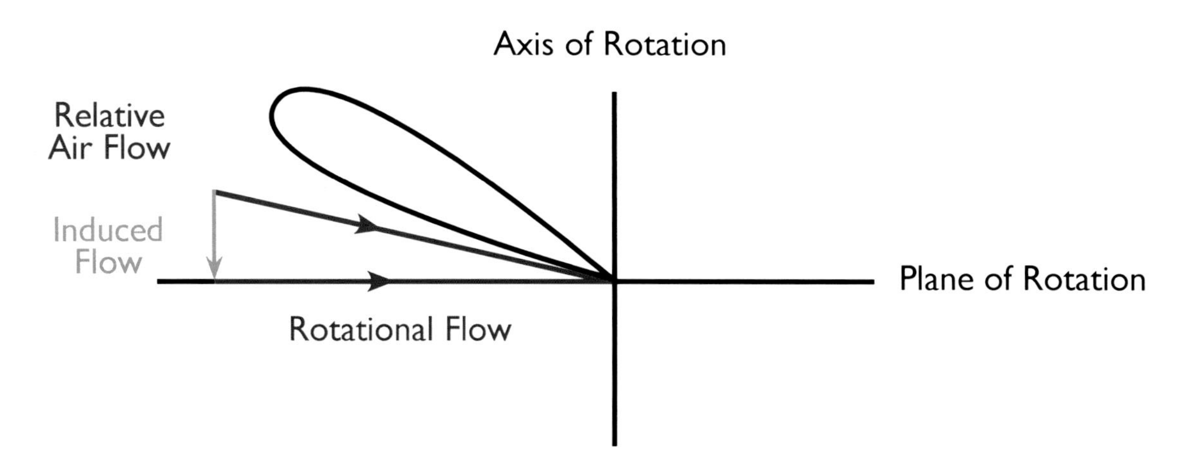

Now a couple of definitions. The line joining the leading and trailing edges of the aerofoil is the chord line; the angle between the chord line and the RAF is the angle of attack; and the angle between the chord line and the plane of rotation is the pitch angle :

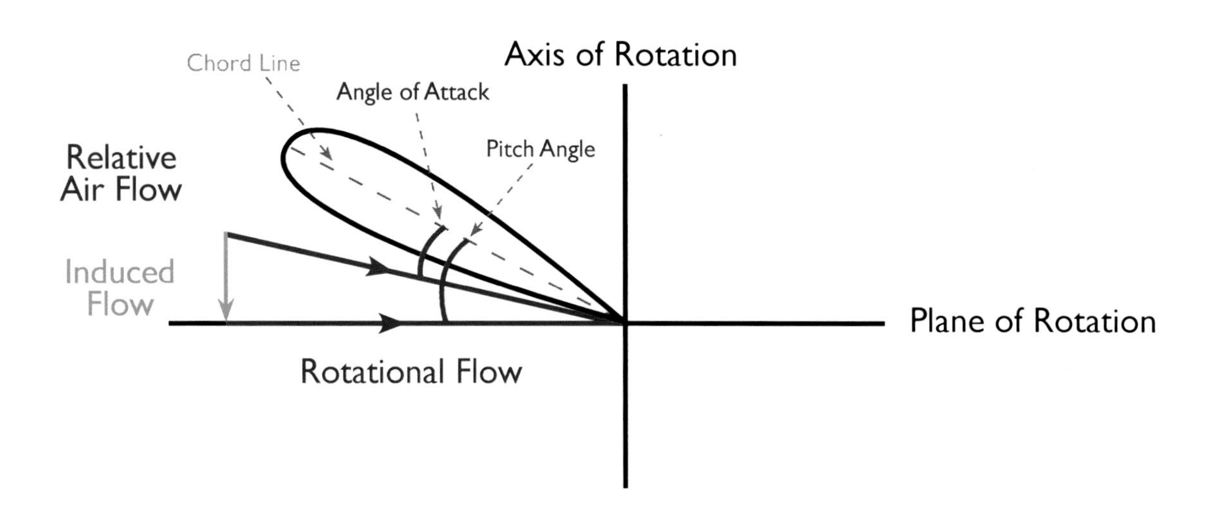

We know that this configuration will produce lift - this is produced at 90° to the relative air flow :

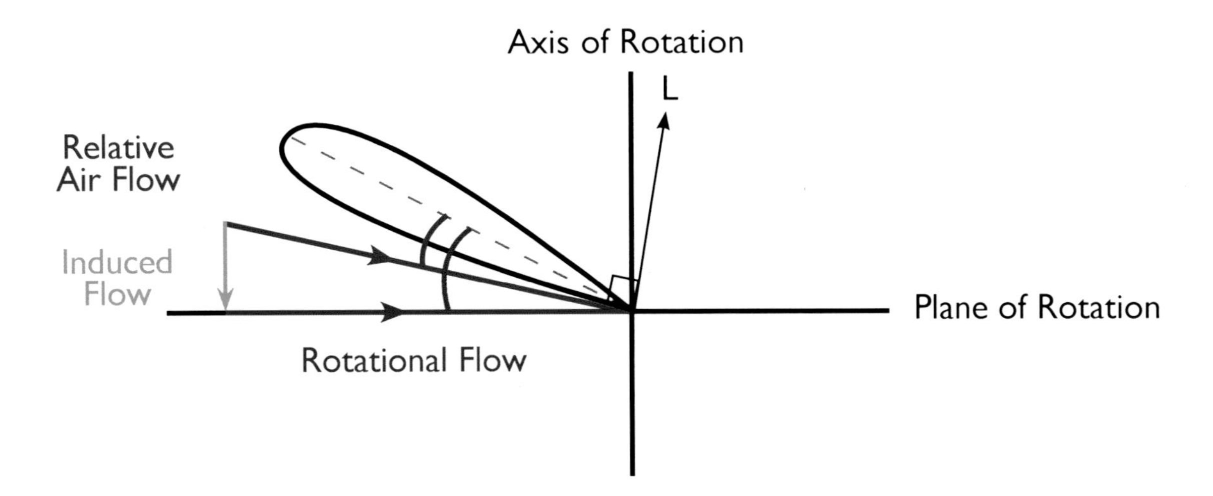

Also drag will be produced, which acts at 90° to the lift :

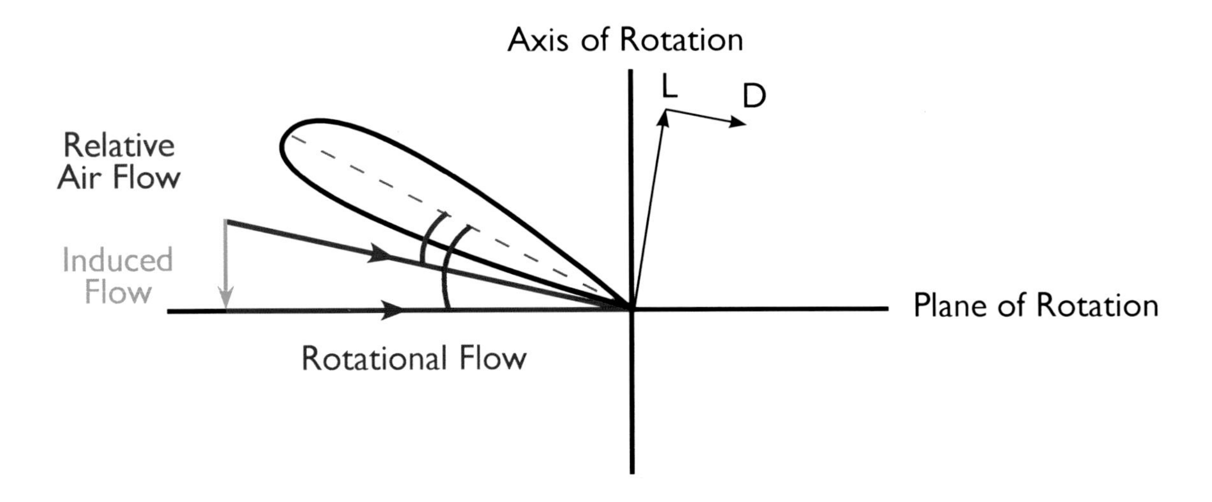

The resultant of the two is the Total Reaction :

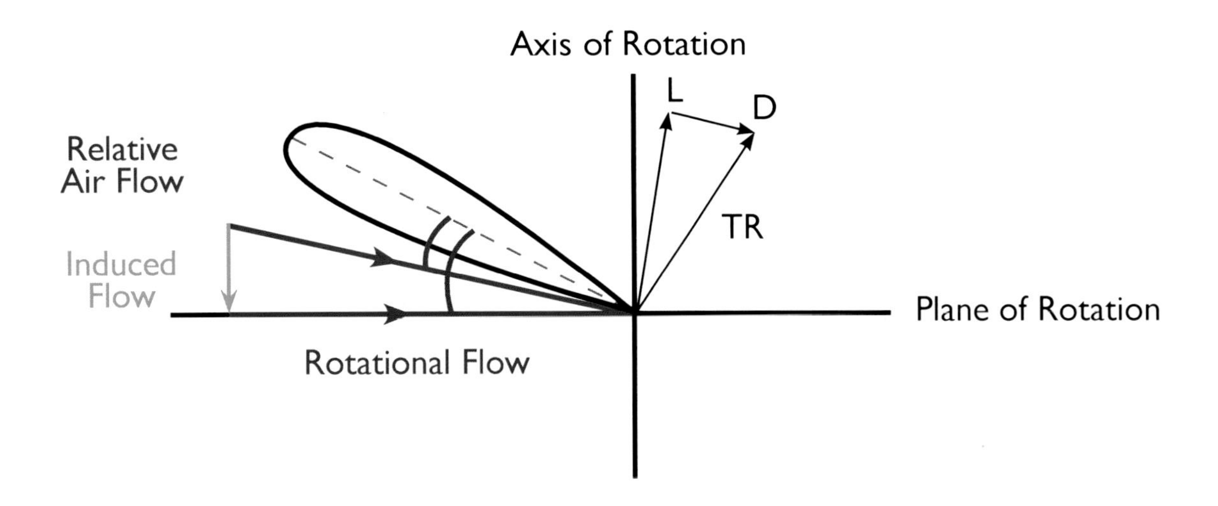

As it stands, we can't use the total reaction, so we take off the vertical component of this, which we call the Rotor Thrust (RT). This opposes the weight of the helicopter. If RT is greater than the weight we go up; if RT is less than the weight we go down :

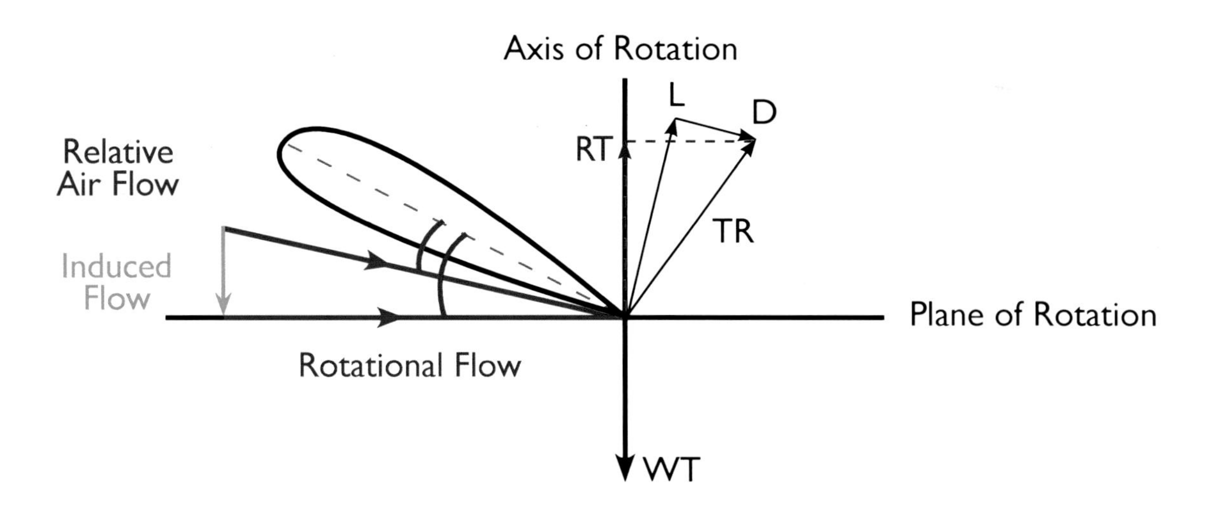

Next we take off the horizontal component of the Rotor Thrust, which we call Rotor Drag. This tries to slow the blade down and is opposed by engine power or torque (Tq). When torque is greater than rotor drag the blade speeds up; when it is less it slows down:

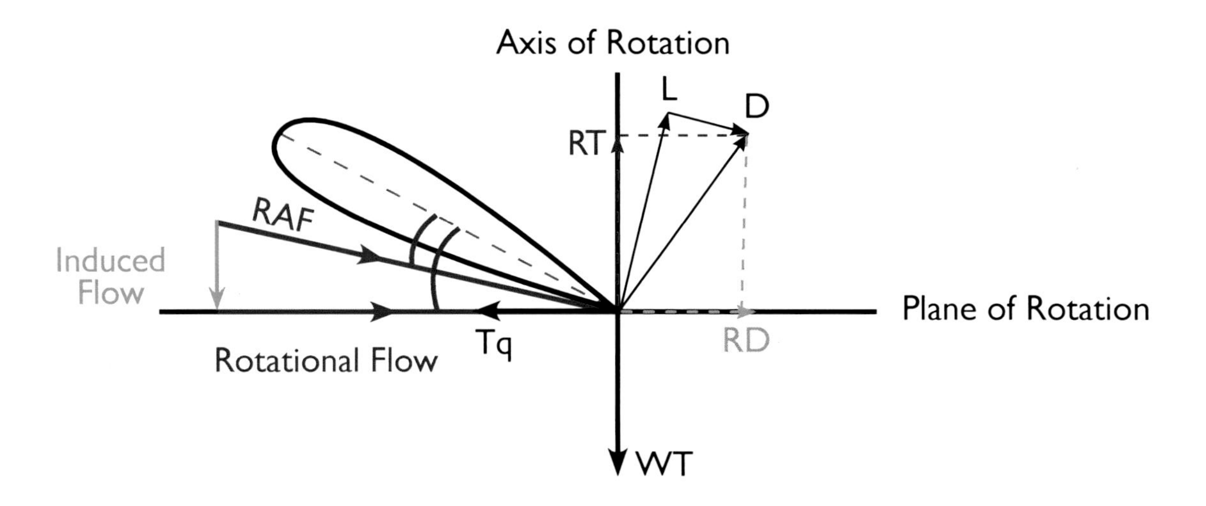

Our vector diagram is now complete.

If you study it for a moment or two, you will see that the key component is induced flow - the big green arrow.

Alter that and everything else alters. For example, for a given pitch angle, if we magically reduce induced flow, then we automatically get a new RAF and increased angle of attack; more angle of attack gives more lift.

This is important for what comes later on - the big green arrow rules, Ok?

Those of you who are entirely logical will have spotted that if you had no induced flow, you would have a very large angle of attack and therefore lots of lift. It follows from this that as induced flow is generated by the blades turning and following one another, you will get maximum lift when the blades are stationary.

Well, ahem, yes, so much for logic! This argument falls about it's ears because with the blades stationary, there is no rotational flow, so the vector diagram only gets started when the blades are turning.

Whilst talking about the blades it is worth mentioning washout. Because a blade goes faster at the tip than at the root, it will experience more lift at the tip than at the root. This will bend the blade up. Washout is a twist built into the blade to make the lift more even from tip to root :

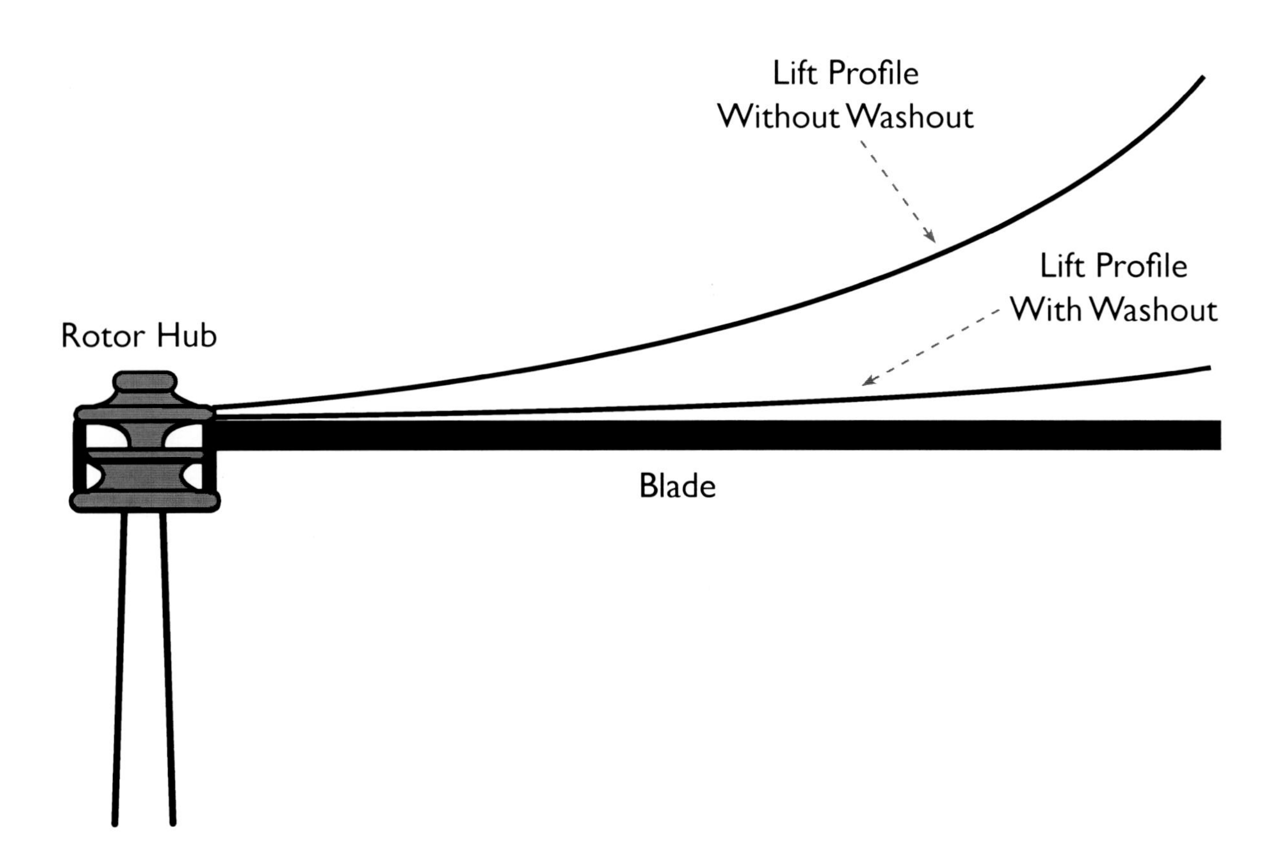

Notes :

We will use the vector diagram to help explain various facets of helicopter flight later, but for the moment let's look at what the controls do. There are 4 main controls; ***cyclic stick, collective lever, throttle and pedals***. Each has a primary and secondary effect. Let's look at the primary effects of each control first.

Cyclic Stick

Some helicopters, like the Enstrom and Schweizer, have a cyclic in front of you, others like the Robinson R22 and R44 have one mounted centrally with a teetering T-bar, a bit like a handlebar on a bike. The T-bar may look a little strange (although with the number of Robinsons being produced it is the others that are now looking strange) but they both do the same job. If you move the cyclic, the movement is transmitted through various linkages and levers etc. (which engineers claim to understand and occasionally tinker with at great expense!) to a swashplate.

This item alters the pitch on the blades. Movement of the cyclic alters pitch on the blades in a cycle - cyclically.

In real language? - Well if you put the cyclic forward...

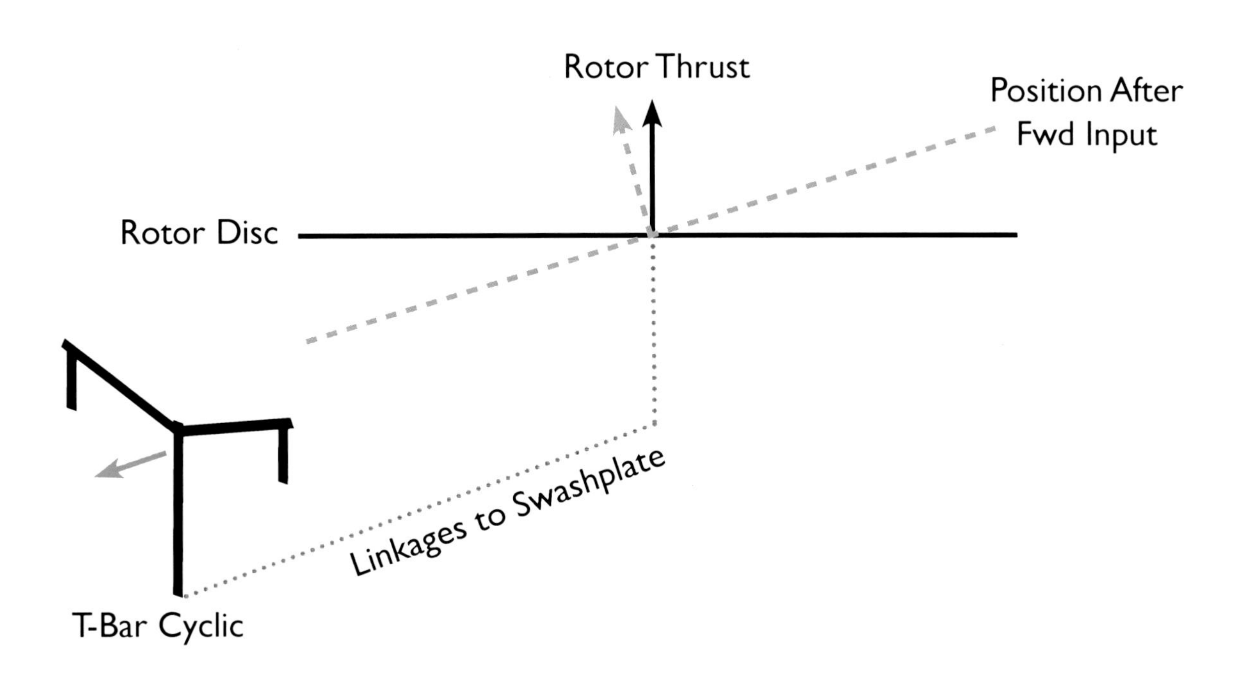

... then you increase the pitch on the blades as they come round to the back of the disc (disc? - sorry, it's the area encompassed by the blades when they're rotating) and reduce the pitch at the front.

The total rotor thrust that was pointing straight up, now points forward and we go forward. Similarly, if we bring the cyclic back we go back, right we go right etc. (if you're old enough to remember the DAF adverts for their cars - forward to go forward, back to go back - it's a bit like that. If you have to ask what a DAF car is - forget it).

Collective Lever

This is the lever which is situated where the handbrake of a car is, but there the similarity ends. The collective, via those linkages, levers and swashplate, alters the pitch on the blades collectively (all together).

Therefore, if you raise the collective lever, pitch angles on the blades are increased, the lift is increased, and the rotor thrust is increased. Therefore, we go up. Lower it and we go down :

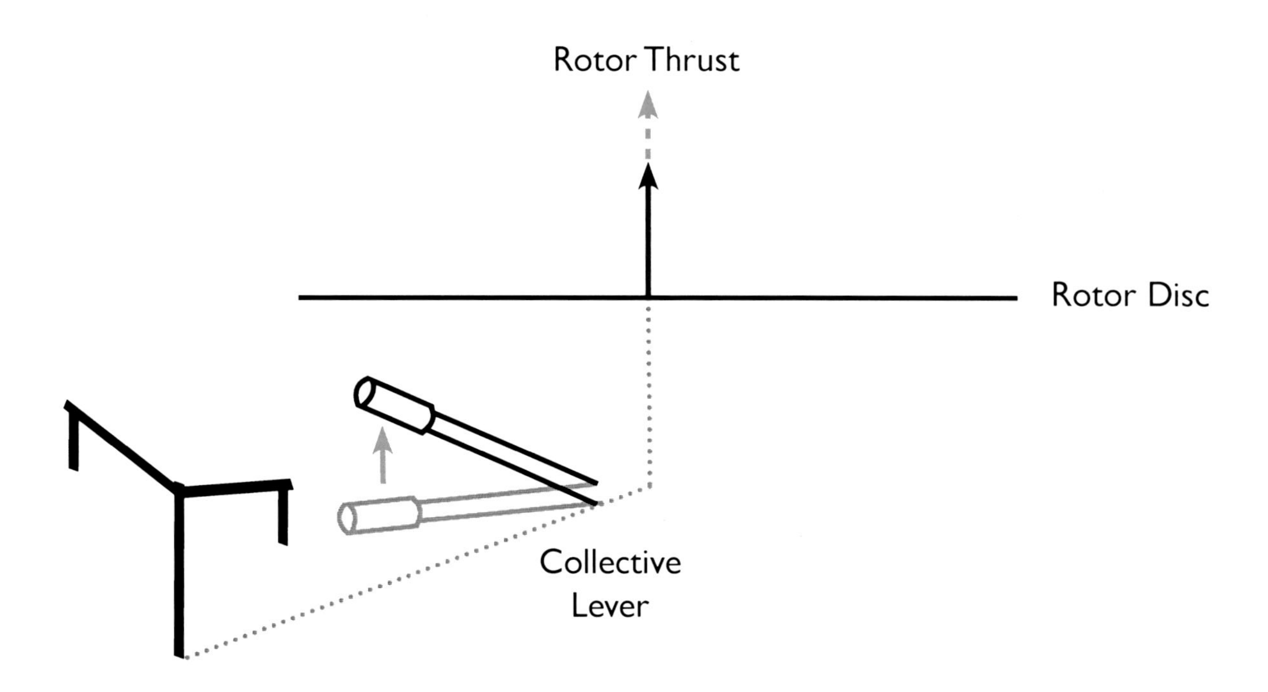

Throttle

The throttle controls the engine RPM and when the engine is turning the blades, the rotor RPM. Just as an aside here, on a piston engined helicopter, we start the engine with the drive from it disconnected from the blades. There wouldn't be enough oomph in the starter motor to turn the engine and the blades. Once we've got the engine going we engage the drive via a clutch, on the Enstrom you pull a damn great lever to engage the clutch, on the Robinson you flick a dinky little switch. If the engine were to seize in flight then you wouldn't want it to stop the blades as well, otherwise it really would be Doomsville with a capital D. So those clever designer chappies have built in a freewheel unit which enables the blades to keep turning when the engine is stopped at idle, just like the freewheel on a bicycle - more of this under "Autorotations". If you are doing the CAA helicopter technical exam beware, there is a question there about clutches and most R22 students get it wrong because they think it refers to a sprag clutch - it doesn't. The CAA call a sprag clutch a freewheel and a clutch a clutch.

Anyway, back to the throttle. To open it you turn it away from you and to close it, towards you; logical except if you are a motorbike rider. With the engine driving the blades both Engine RPM and Rotor RPM will increase when you open the throttle, Manifold Air Pressure (MAP) - a measure of how hard the engine is working - will also increase (on a piston engined helicopter).

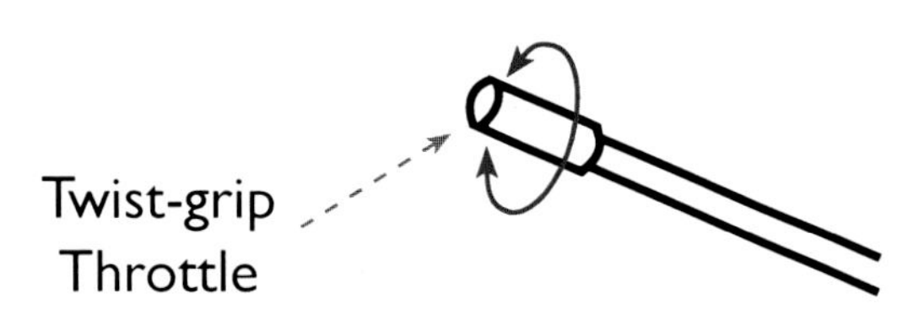

Pedals

No, they're not rudder pedals, because we don't have a rudder. If you're reading this in your machine and you can see a rudder behind you, then you're probably in a Cessna 152. If you put an engine on one end of a shaft and use it to turn the shaft and blades mounted on the other end of the shaft, then the body of the engine will try to turn in the opposite direction of rotation of the blades. This is called Torque Reaction. Mount the engine in the body of a helicopter and the body will similarly turn :

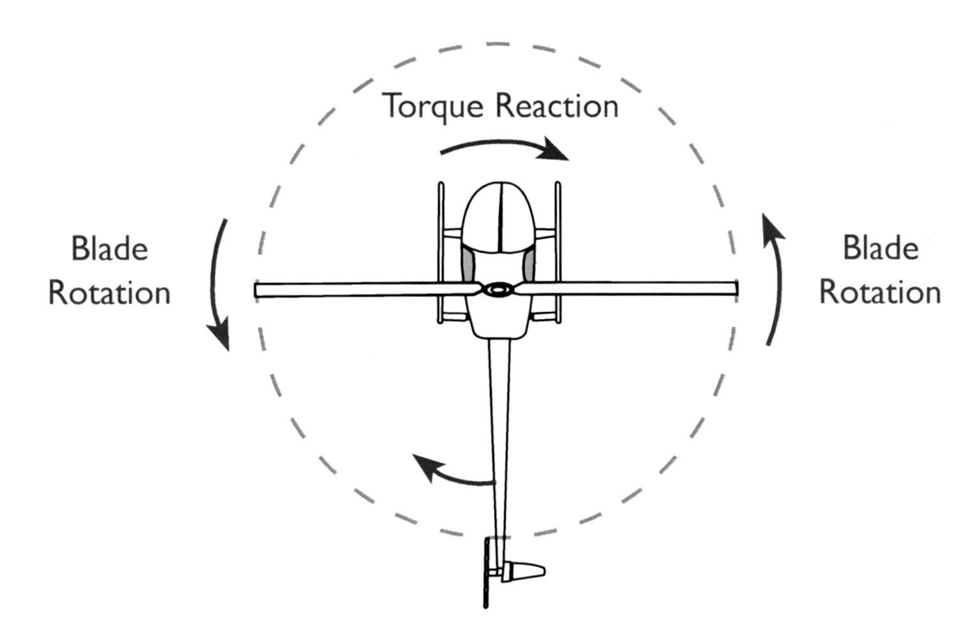

The tail rotor generates lift sideways and the pitch on the tail rotor is varied by the pedals. So, by using the pedals, we can (most of the time) stop the helicopter spinning uncontrollably when we leave the ground; turn the helicopter in the hover and fly the helicopter in balance when in forward flight.

These are the main (primary) effects of the controls :

Cyclic - forward to go forward and increase speed; back to go back and reduce speed; left to go left; right to go right or any combination of the above.

Collective - up to go up and down to go down.

Throttle - open - more RPM; close - less RPM.

Pedals - left pedal - nose goes left; right pedal - nose goes right.

On the next page we will look at some of the secondary effects of each control.

Cyclic Stick - Secondary Effects

If in forward flight we ease the cyclic forward (don't push, helicopters like to be treated gently) then as we increase the speed, two things happen - firstly we go down. This is because we have tilted the total rotor thrust forwards, whilst we have the same total amount, we have less vertical component. Therefore we go down, unless we raise the lever at the same time - your instructor will teach you about this.

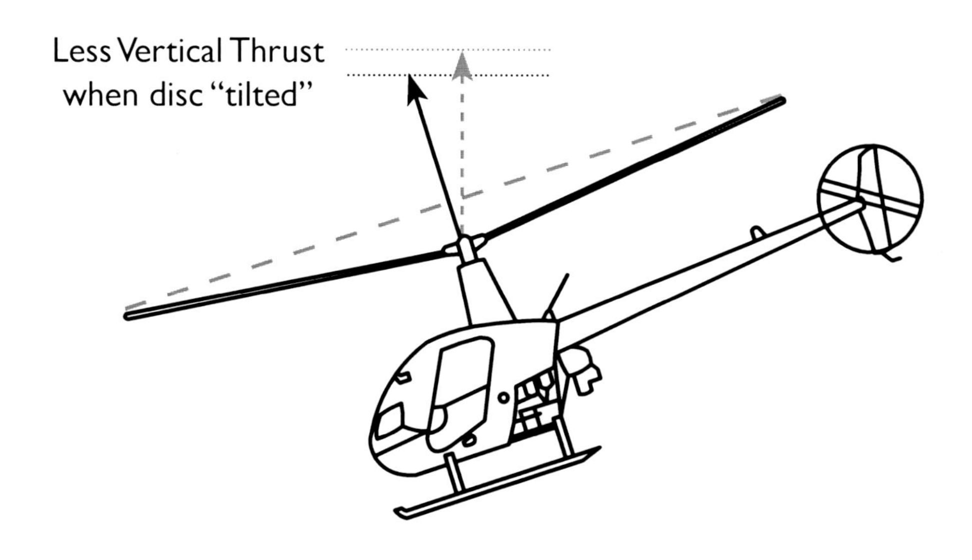

Secondly, the rotor RPM will increase. This is because as we increase speed we get increased wind across the disc which blows away some of the induced flow :

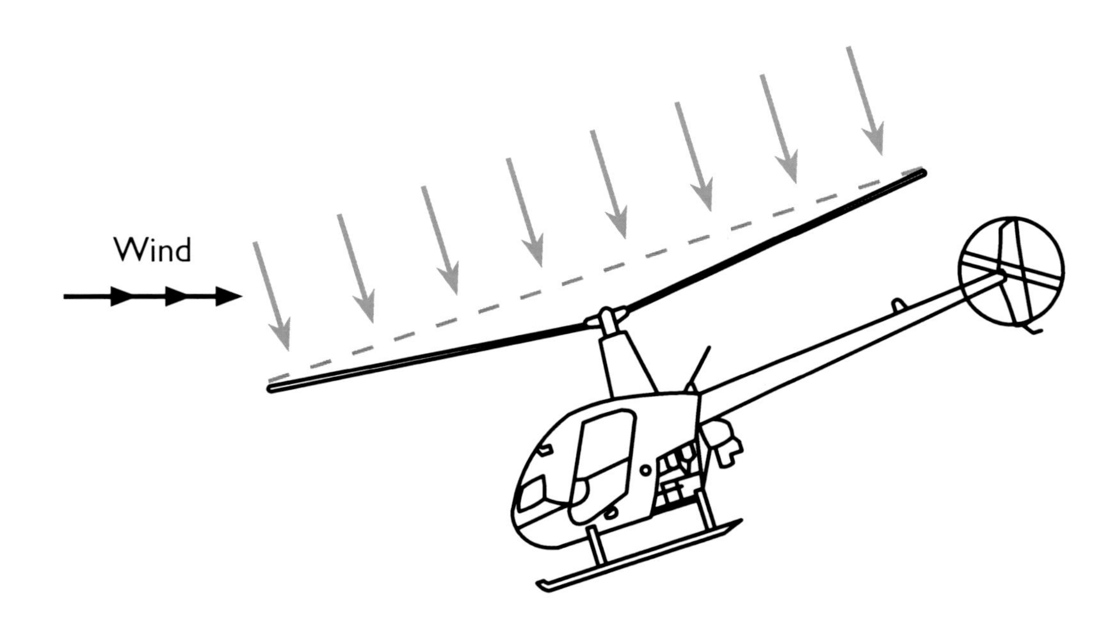

Back to the vector diagram (here's one I prepared earlier) :

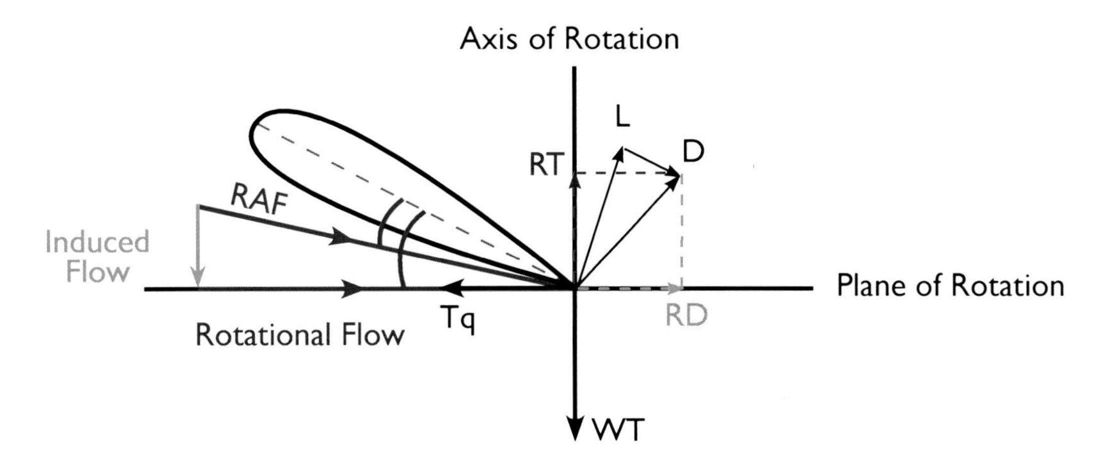

If we reduce the induced flow, then we get a new relative air flow, and from a given pitch angle, an increased angle of attack :

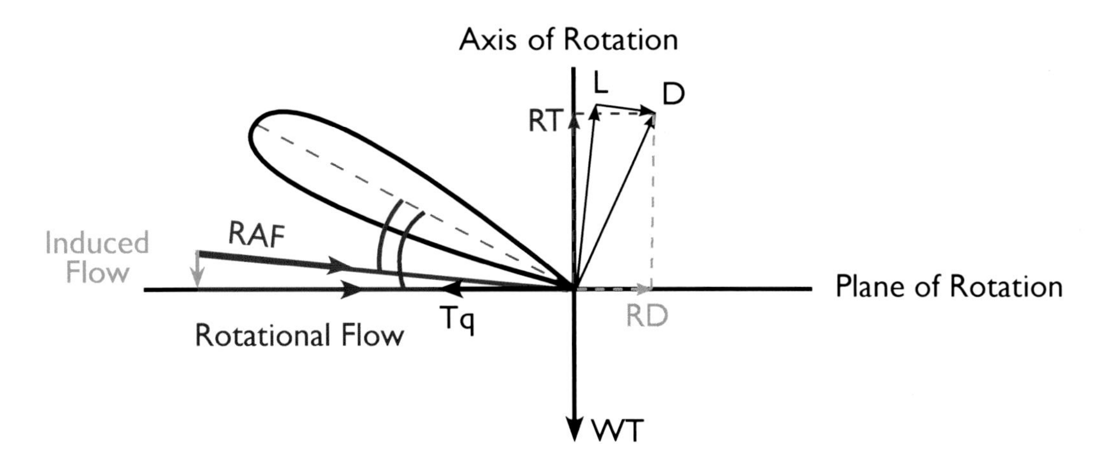

Lift is increased, but because it acts 90° to the RAF, it moves forward, towards the axis of rotation. This also moves the increased drag forward. The net result is that we have a reduction in rotor drag. Therefore, less drag, rotor RPM (RRPM) increases. We won't go up because we have tilted the rotor thrust and therefore have less vertical component. A lot of what we are going to do involves working with the vector diagram like this, so it is important that you can follow this explanation. If you can't, keep going over it until you can.

Still on the cyclic, if we flare the helicopter - pull back on the stick - we load the disc (i.e. the helicopter feels an increase in 'g' or apparent weight) causing the blade to cone up. The coning angle, incidentally, is the angle between the blade and the Tip Path Plane:

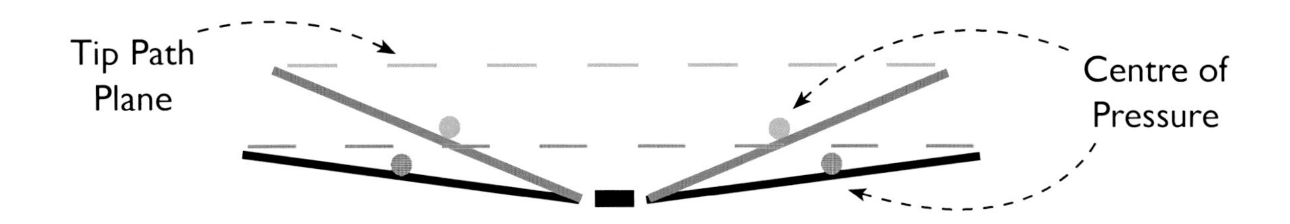

Because the blades cone up, the centre of pressure moves inwards and due to ***coriolis*** the blades speed up.
Coriolis? Just think about an ice skater. If she brings her arms in she speeds up, if she puts them out she slows down. By the same token if you ease the cyclic forward to offload the disc, then the RRPM will reduce.

Collective Lever - Secondary Effects

Three things happen when you raise the lever :

Firstly the aircraft's nose will tend to yaw (if you don't know what yaw is, please see Appendix 1) in the opposite direction to the direction of rotation of the rotor blades, due to torque reaction.

Secondly the RRPM will reduce. Back to the vector diagram :

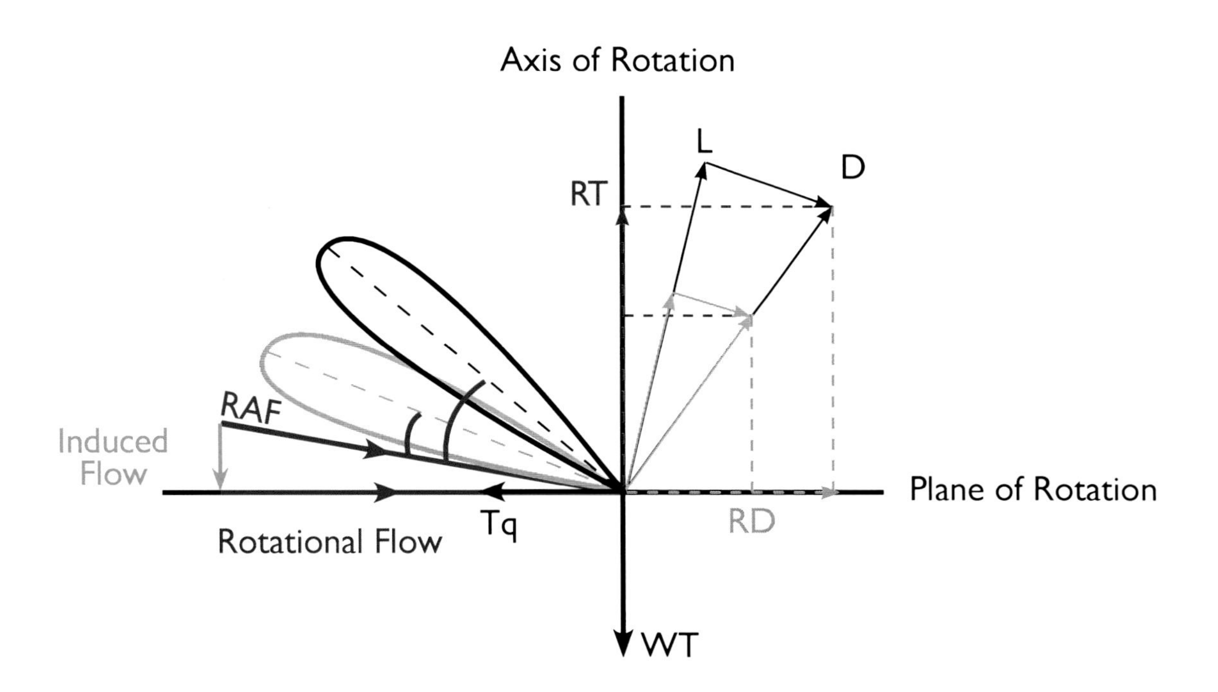

If you increase the pitch angle, then the angle of the attack will increase and so will lift, but also more importantly, so will rotor drag, therefore the RRPM will reduce. On older types of piston helicopters this meant that you had to increase throttle to increase torque, balancing the increased rotor drag (which in turn meant more yaw due to torque reaction). Now many have a correlator to keep RRPM controlled. Others have a governor, similar to that fitted to turbine engine helicopters.

Thirdly, the nose of the helicopter will pitch up. This is due to the increased downwash on the rear stabiliser.

If we lower the collective then the opposite of all these will occur.

Due to the correlator, the Manifold Air Pressure will also increase or decrease with alteration in lever. MAP therefore varies with both lever and throttle. It is possible to over-MAP and over-Torque the helicopter. Over MAP'ing is simply making the engine work harder, pushing out more power, than it was meant to. With over-Torqueing you stress the transmission system.

If the power required to maintain Total Rotor Thrust remains the same but Rotor RRPM is reduced, then the torque from the engine will increase and may exceed the design limitations of the transmission.

Throttle - Secondary Effects

As noted above, throttle varies torque and therefore the torque reaction. To maintain balanced flight, pedals will be needed. Your instructor will show you this. Here we are concerned with how a helicopter flies, not how to fly it.

Pedals - Secondary Effects

When we put more pitch on the tail rotor by using the pedals we increase the drag on the tail rotor. The vector diagram for the tail rotor works exactly the same as the main rotor, so I won't repeat it.

The point is that the power drive from the engine goes to both the main and the tail rotor, putting more drag on the tail rotor also slows down the main rotor slightly, by a couple of percent RRPM.

Most of the above RRPM changes will be masked by a modern governor system, such as that fitted to the R22, but will still be seen if it is switched off or if you are unfortunate enough to fly a machine without a governor.

Notes :

Your instructor will teach you how to get into a hover (which pedal to use to overcome torque reaction etc.), but I want to look at the aerodynamics of hovering.

First of all, let's hover clear of the ground, this is called out of the ground effect (OGE). You'll find out what ground effect is in a minute.

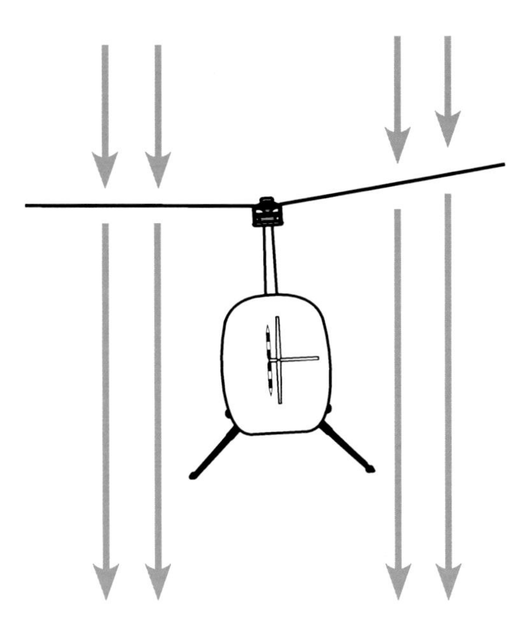

Now let's put the ground just beneath the helicopter :

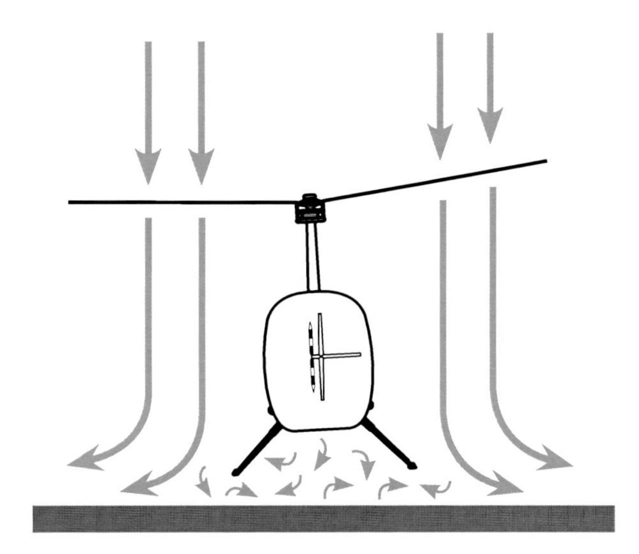

The induced flow, instead of just flowing downwards, hits the ground. Some goes outwards, some goes inwards where it meets and forms a sort of dome of slightly higher pressure. This is called hovering in ground effect (IGE).

This restricts the flow of the induced flow through the disc. Onto the vector diagram - less induced flow, greater angle of attack (for a given pitch angle) greater lift and we go up :

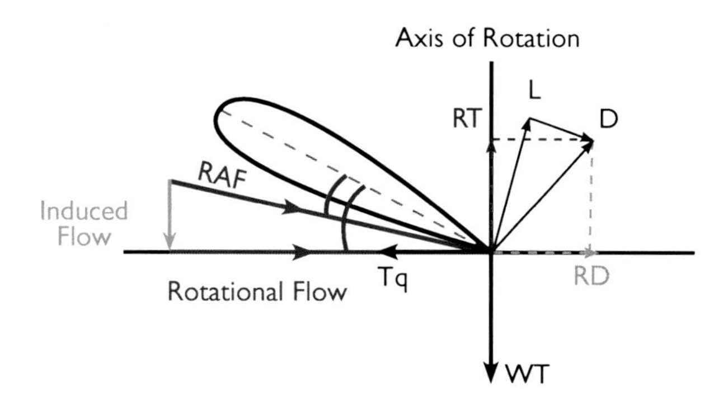

OGE Hover - More Induced Flow

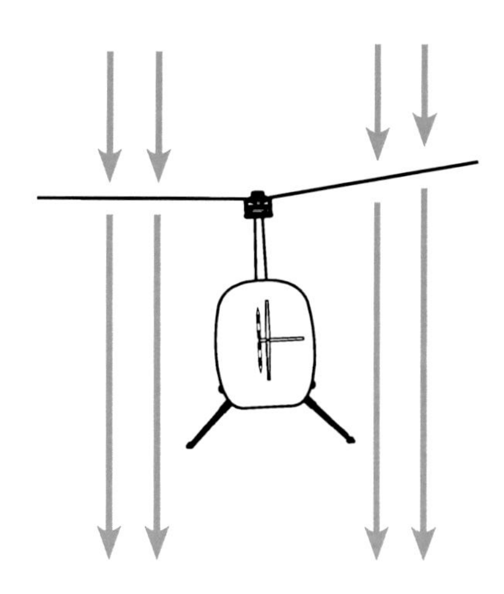

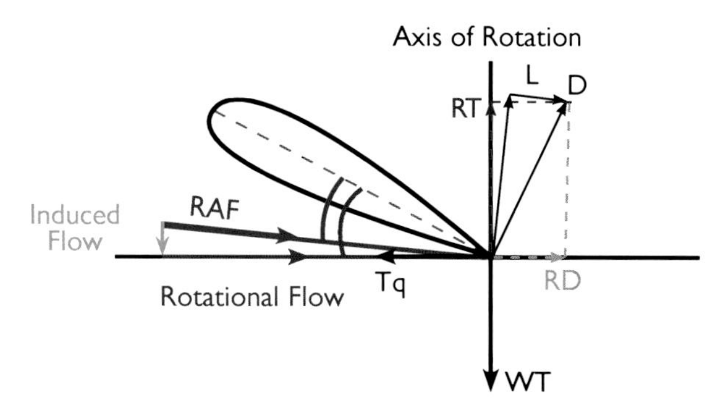

IGE Hover - Less Induced Flow

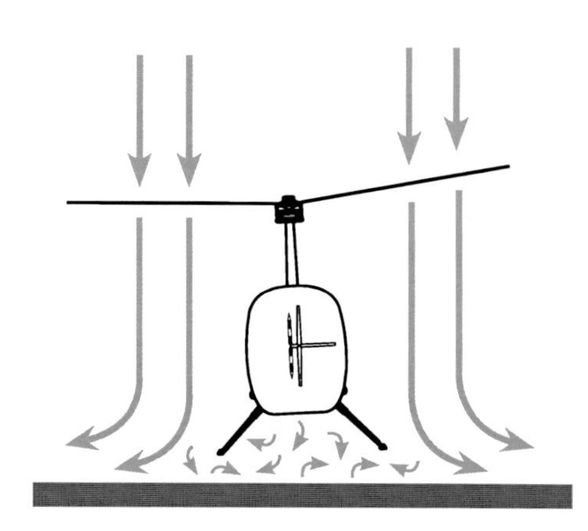

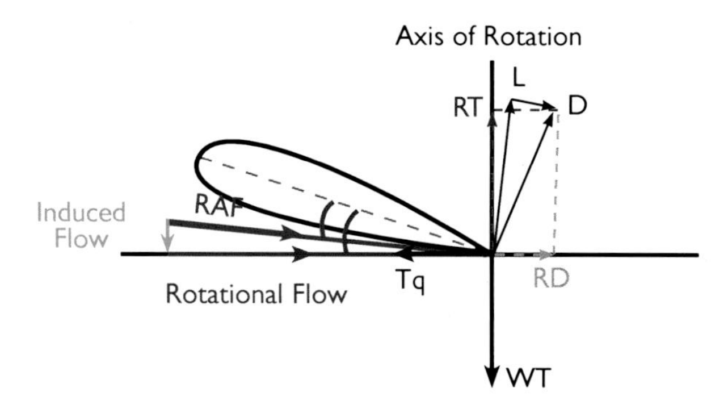

Less Drag Therefore Less Power

In fact, we reduce the pitch angle to restore the angle of attack. Less pitch angle means less rotor drag and therefore less power to oppose rotor drag. Therefore, in ground effect, or on the ground cushion, we can hover with less power.

The ground cushion will be affected by a number of factors :

1. On a slope it will tend to slip downhill
2. On long grass it will tend to be dissipated
3. It will be more noticeable and make the aircraft more skittish, on tarmac or concrete
4. On a windy day it will be blown behind the helicopter
5. It tends to disappear if you hover at a height over approximately 2/3 the rotor diameter

Now supposing we hover next to a building. The induced flow which was hitting the ground and flowing from the helicopter now hits the building, goes up the side and gets sucked into the disc - recirculates - increasing the induced flow :

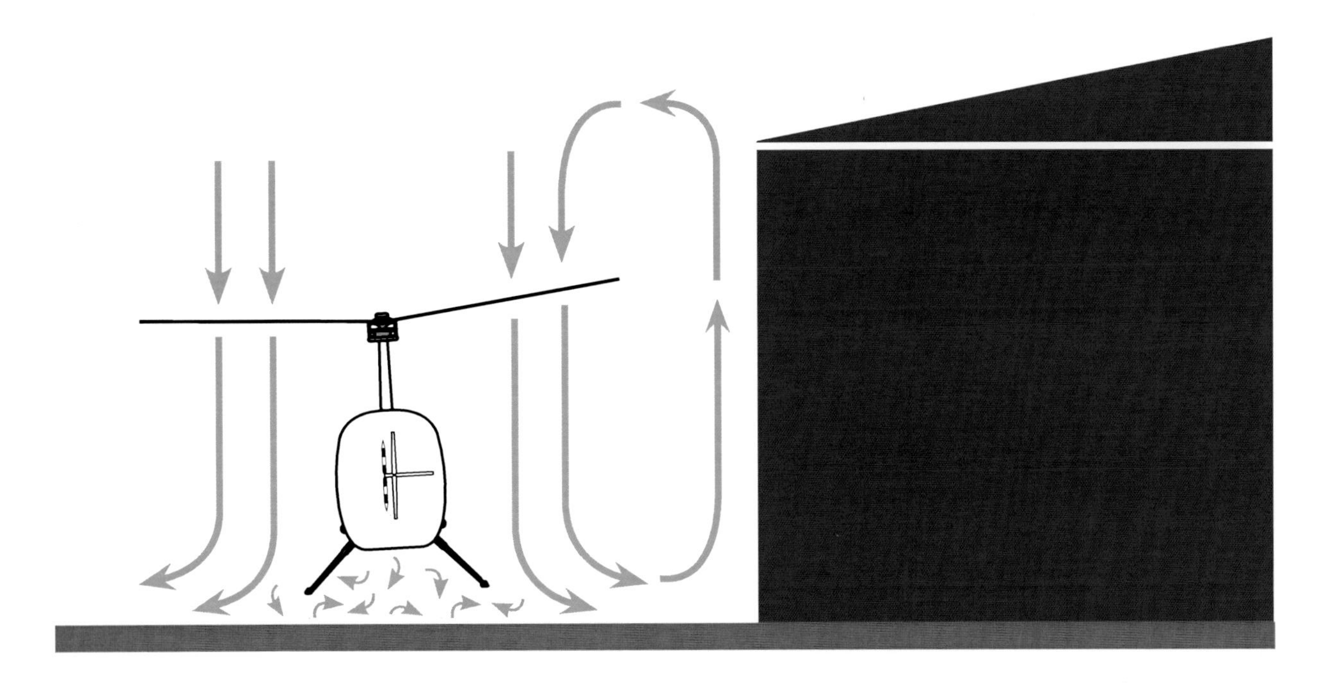

Increasing the induced flow means less lift (I'll skip the tortuous logic - if you can't follow, go back to Chapter 1).

Therefore there will be less lift over that part of the disc where recirculation is occurring, and the helicopter will tend to move, if not corrected with cyclic, towards the building :

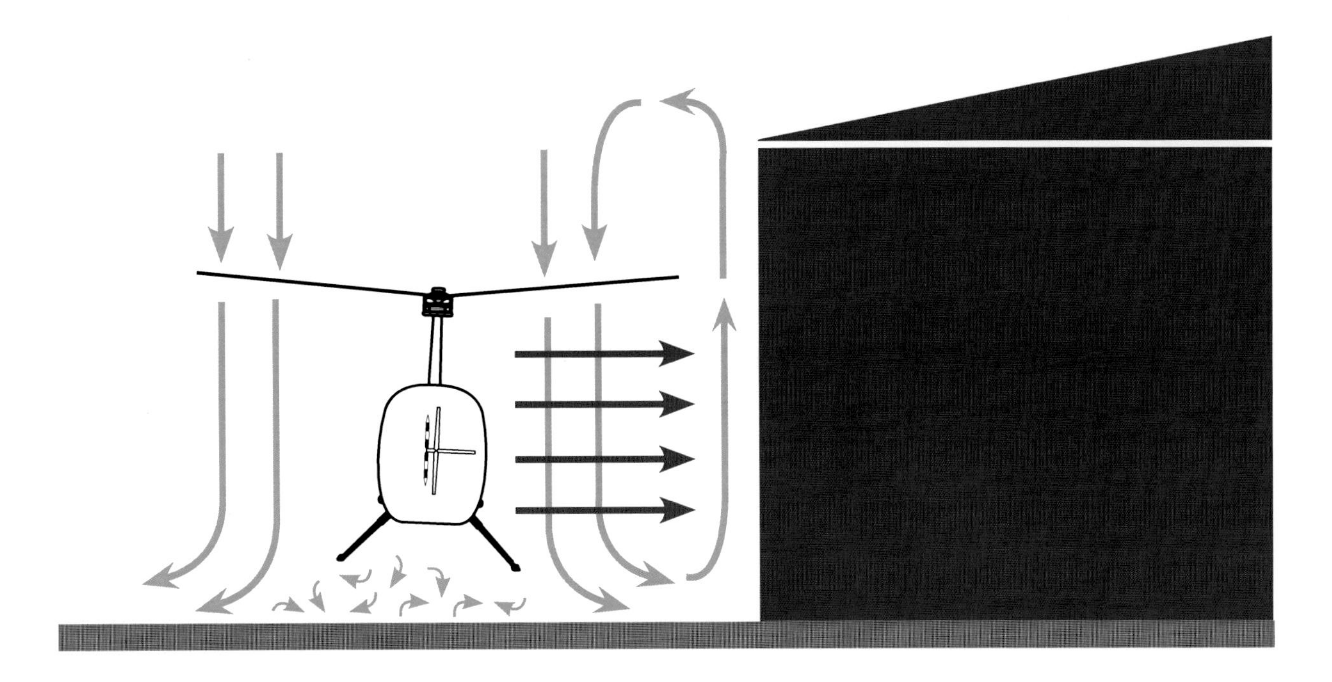

Most helicopters hover one skid low. This is due to Tail Rotor Drift. You what? Well, let's go back to torque reaction, and illustrate a helicopter as a bar :

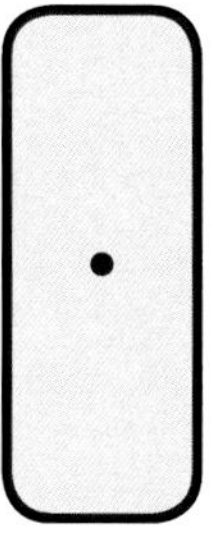

On the top of this let's put the rotor disc :

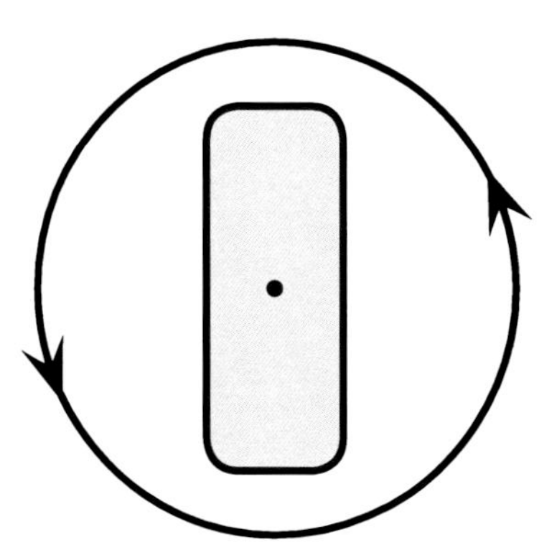

Now if the blades go round anti-clockwise, the helicopters body will tend to turn clockwise (torque reaction) :

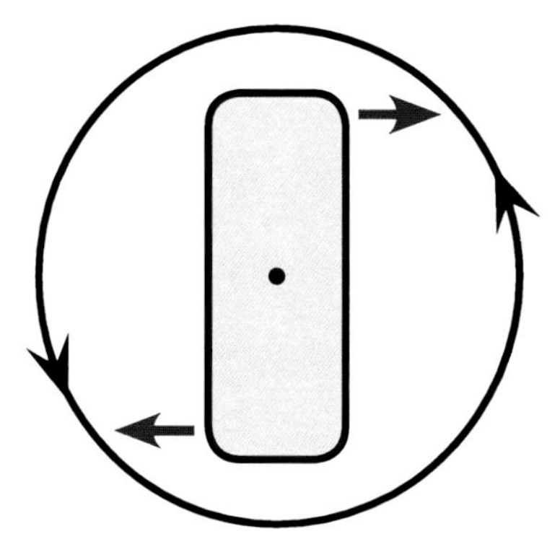

We could stop this by putting a small rotor on the front left of the helicopter and one on the tail right :

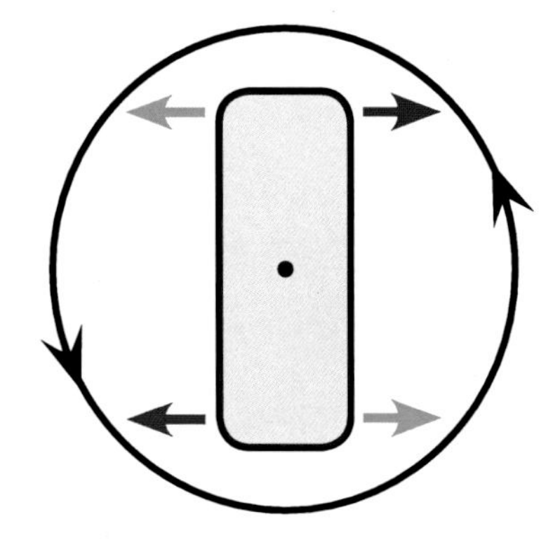

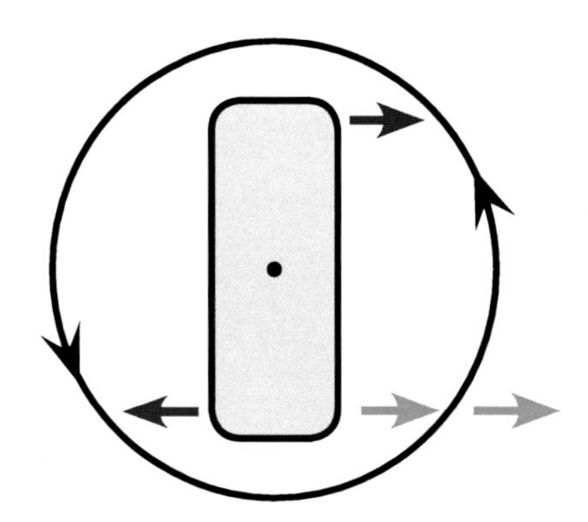

This is exactly what happened on some early designs (don't worry Enstrom and Bell 47 owners, I mean very early designs). In fact, it was found to be more effective to dispense with the rotor at the nose and put twice the force at the tail.

Now there are three forces pulling the helicopter to the right and only one to the left, which means that the helicopter will drift to the right. This is known as tail rotor drift.

This can be countered by the pilot applying left cyclic, or partially in the design stage by offsetting the mast and/or tail rotor. The more astute amongst you will have noticed that few helicopters have a tail rotor mounted on the right of the tail, but that the majority have them mounted on the left. They still develop a push force to the right, but are mounted on the left for design considerations which we need not concern ourselves with here.

With tail rotor drift comes tail rotor roll. What happens here is that when the pilot applies left cyclic to correct for tail rotor drift, this causes the helicopter to hover left skid low, but also moves the tail rotor out to the right.

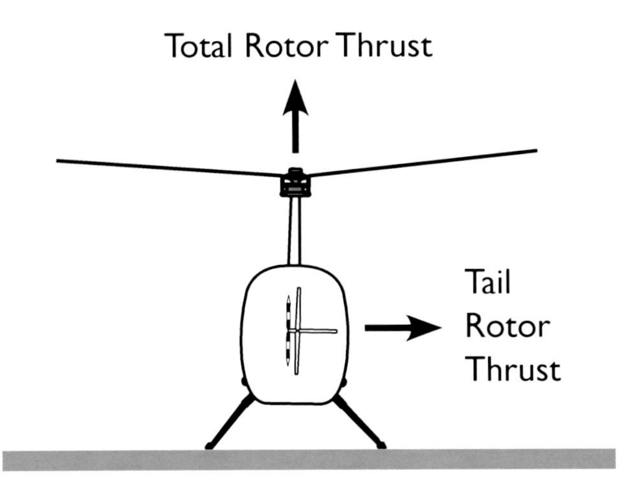

Helicopter on the ground
(viewed from the rear)

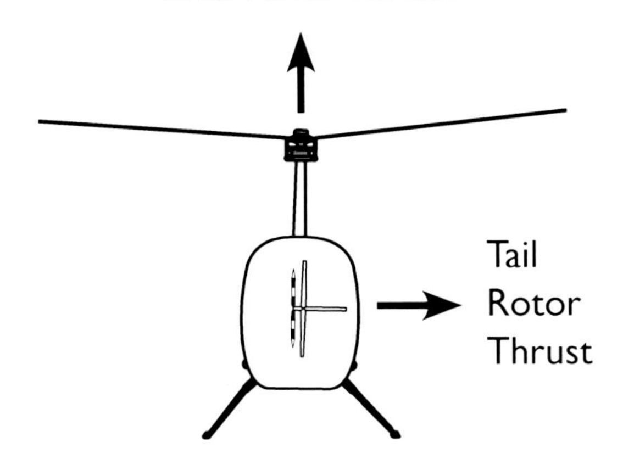

Helicopter lifts to hover and drifts right due to tail rotor drift

A rolling couple is now set up which makes the aircraft roll more. Tail rotor roll ceases when the rolling couple forces are equal, i.e. when the tail rotor thrust and the total rotor thrust are in the same plane either vertically or horizontally.

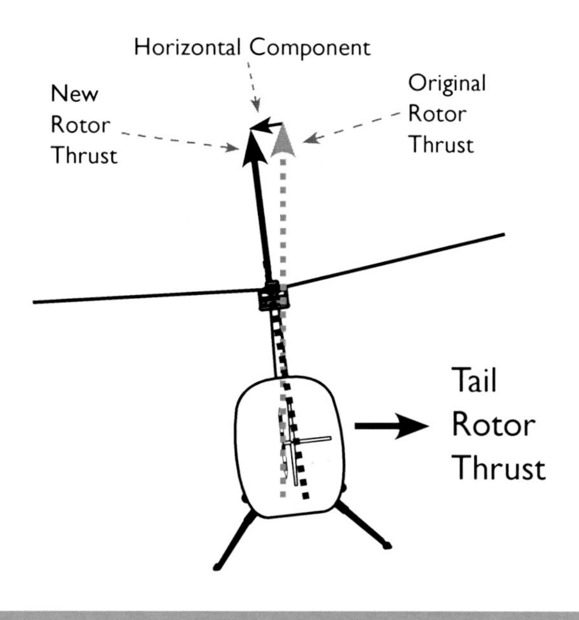

Left cyclic applied to correct rolling couple set up between horizontal component of total rotor thrust and tail rotor thrust

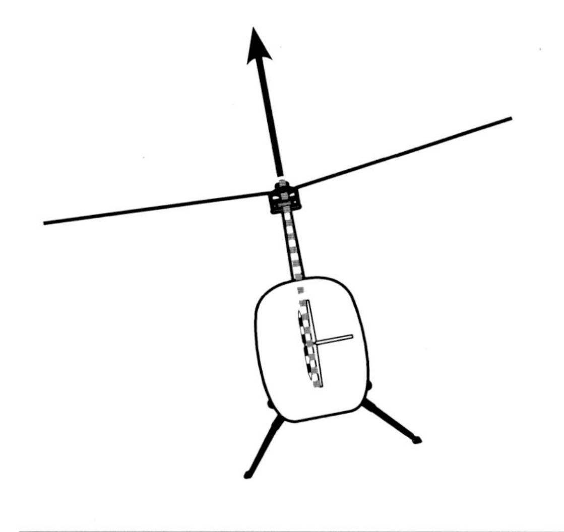

Tail rotor thrust is now in line with rotor thrust in the vertical plane - no tail rotor roll - but helicopter ends up hovering left skid low

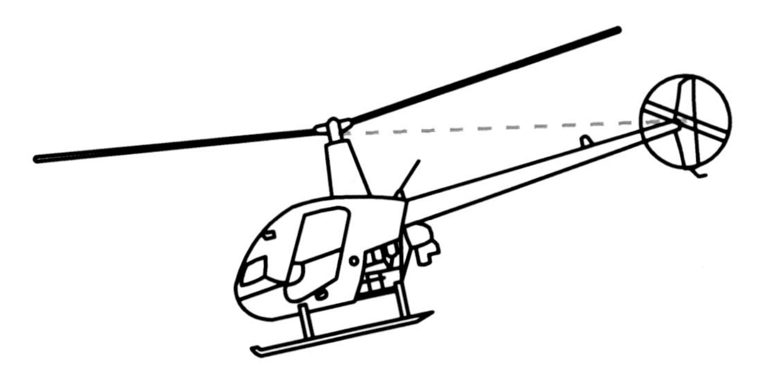

In forward flight, nose down attitude causes tail rotor thrust to be in line with rotor thrust in the horizontal plane - therefore no tail rotor roll

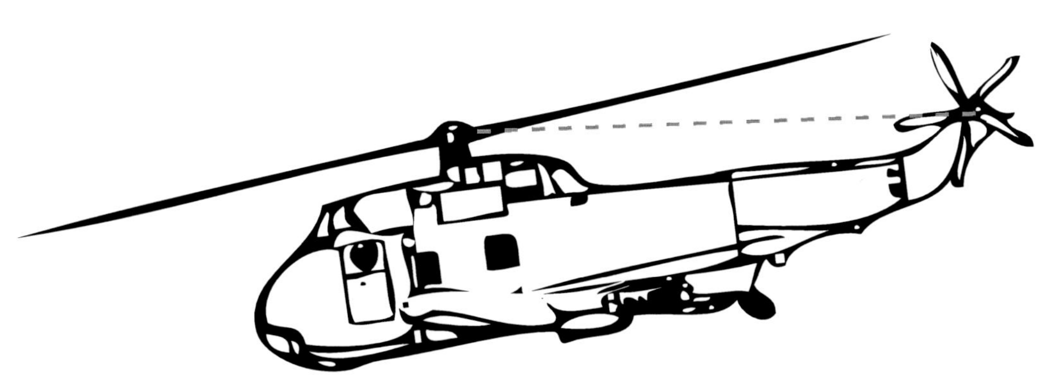

Some larger helicopters have their tail rotor mounted on a pylon to make sure there is no tail rotor roll in forward flight

At this point it is convenient to discuss ground resonance. This doesn't occur in the hover, but as its name applies, when the aircraft is in contact with the ground. This will, of course, happen when taking off or landing.

The helicopter is always naturally vibrating, but when two vibrations are present of sympathetic frequency, the vibration will build up. If you consider troops marching across a bridge, if they are in step they can set up a vibration on the bridge which builds up until the bridge breaks. The swaying on the Millenium Bridge in London when it opened in 2000 was initially thought by some to be caused by this. In fact the vibration was not vertical (which the designers had allowed for) but lateral caused by the pressure which people exert when they walk, now known as Synchronous Lateral Excitation. Not a lot to do with helicopters - I just thought that it was interesting.

The sympathetic vibrations in a helicopter can be set up by a pilot mishandling, blades of unequal weight or balance (ice or damage), out of track blades, varying tyre or oleo (gas filled struts to soften the landing) pressures, and landing with one wheel or skid on concrete and the other on grass.

Once started, ground resonance can develop very quickly and the helicopter could shake itself to pieces! Prevention, through knowledge and correct handling is better than cure, but if it does occur the RRPM should be altered by shutting down, or the ground contact broken by taking off.

Notes :

During the transition from the hover to forward flight, a number of interesting things happen. Again, your instructor will, for a few silver coins, show you how to overcome these effects and execute a perfect transition. Here we will merely examine what they are :

1. Loss of Height

As you move forward you lose height. Firstly, because you are tilting the thrust vector you have less vertical component of thrust and you will therefore go down. Secondly, you lose height because you move off the ground cushion :

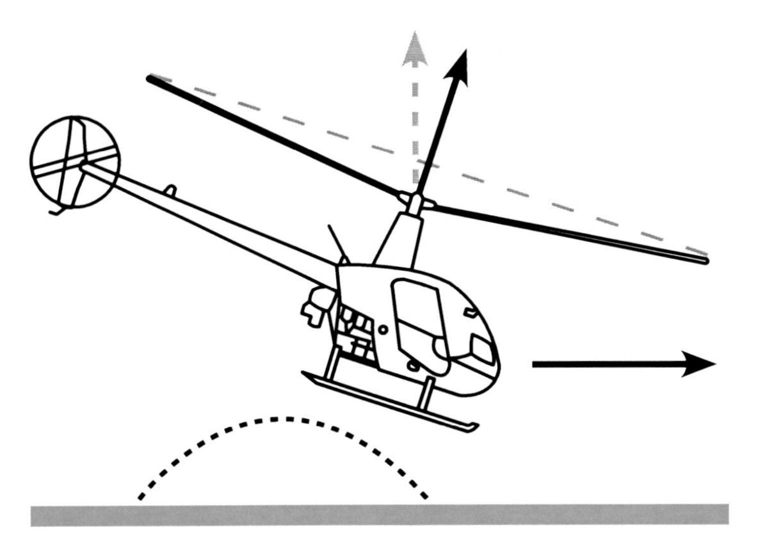

Aircraft moves off the ground cushion and has left vertical component of rotor thrust, therefore it loses height.

2. Flapback

When you increase speed from the hover, the disc tends to flapback. The same happens in forward flight and by the time you get to transitioning you should already have been shown this effect. What happens is that as you go forward you get a bit more airspeed. A rotor going round has Velocity of Rotation (Vr). The blade now going into the wind you have created by going forward will have Velocity of Rotation, and Velocity of the Wind (Vw), whilst the blade going downwind will have Velocity of Rotation minus Velocity of Wind.

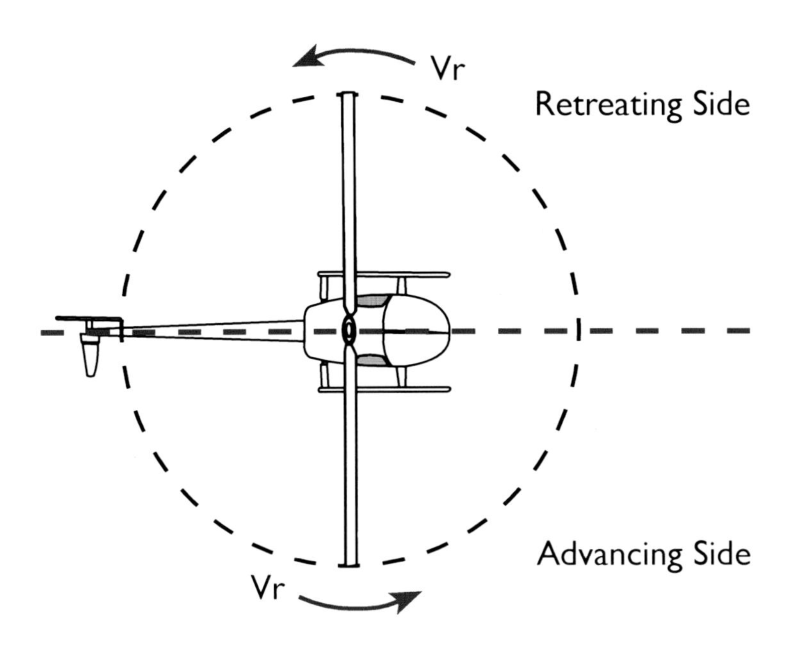

The rotor disc viewed from above. Both sides of the disc, the advancing and retreating view have velocity of rotation, Vr.

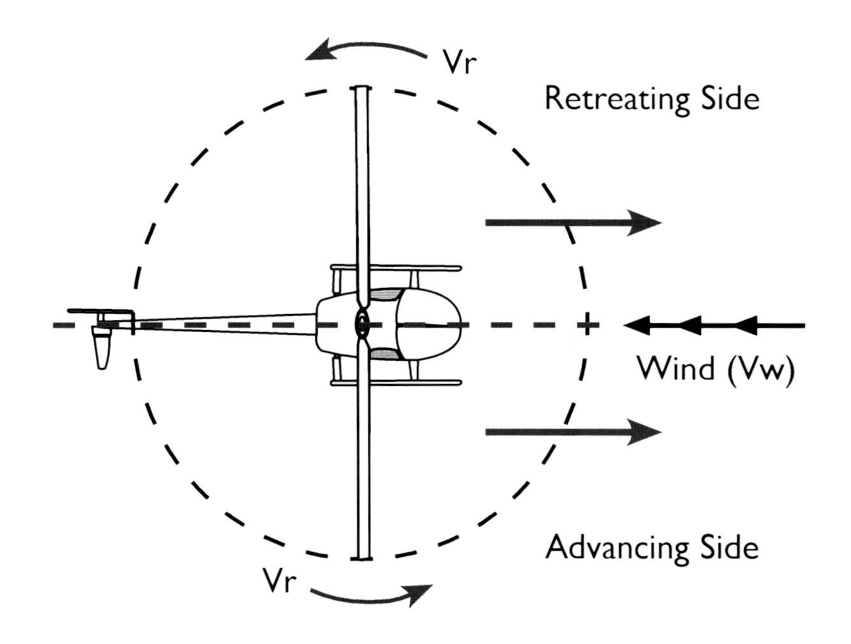

Aircraft now starts to move forward, inducing a wind across the disc (Vw).

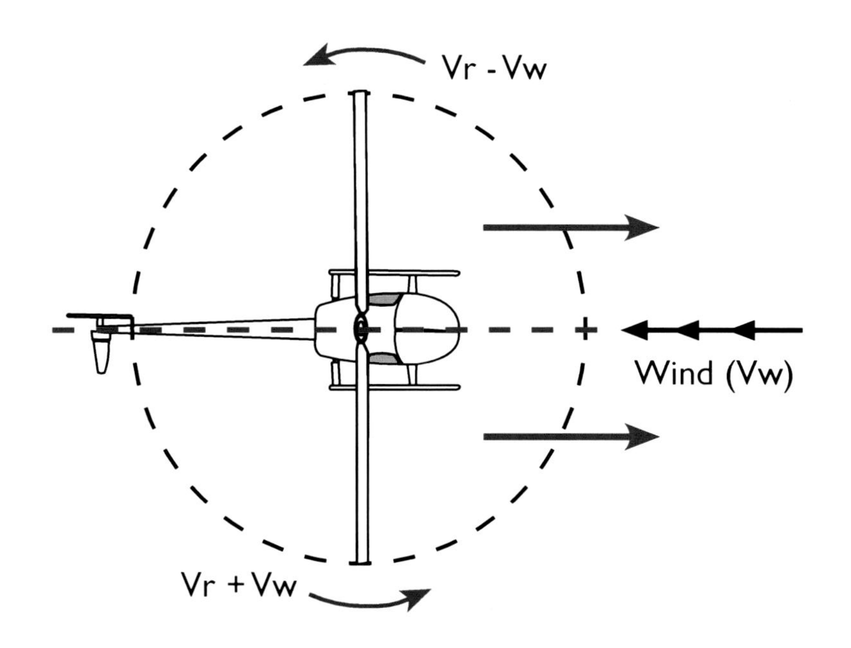

Advancing blade now has velocity of rotation and wind, (Vr + Vw) and the retreating blade velocity of rotation minus wind (Vr - Vw).

This is the formula for lift :

$$\textbf{Lift} = C_L \tfrac{1}{2}\rho V^2 S$$

CL = coefficient of lift. This is designed into the blade and is therefore constant.

1/2 is the fraction 1/2 (half).

p is the greek letter regarding density, which at any given height will be constant across the disc.

V is the velocity of the blade.

S is the surface area of the blade, which is constant.

Out of the Lift forumula the only variable element is V. The advancing blade will have more V (Vr + Vw) and more lift, and will therefore rise whilst the velocity of the retreating blade will have less V (Vr - Vw) and less lift, and will therefore descend. From the cockpit you will therefore see the front of the disc go up (whilst the back of the disc goes down). The disc has "flapped" back and the nose of the aircraft will follow.

Therefore whilst you may have gained a couple of knots, the disc will be back where it started and you will stop accelerating. In order to keep accelerating forward you will need to move the cyclic moving forward again to overcome flapback.

The disc may also flap when the helicopter is starting up or shutting down. Because the disc is less rigid at low RRPM, a gust of wind may make the disc flap back; conversely if a sharp gust of wind dies away, the disc may flap forward. This is why there are wind limitations on starting and stopping rotors and generally why you do not clear people into the disc area during starting and stopping. When the disc is going slowly, individual blades may flap up and down under the affecting wind; this is called blade sailing.

3. Translational Lift

This is simply free lift generated by the fact that you are going fowards. As you go forwards you get airflow across the disc which, in effect, blows away some of the induced flow. Less induced flow means a new relative airflow and, for a given pitch angle, a greater angle of attack and therefore more lift. Voila!

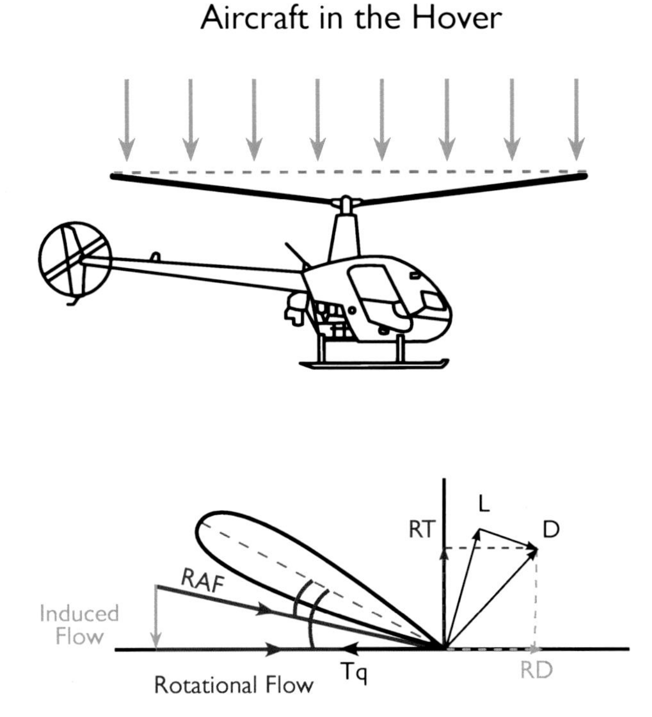

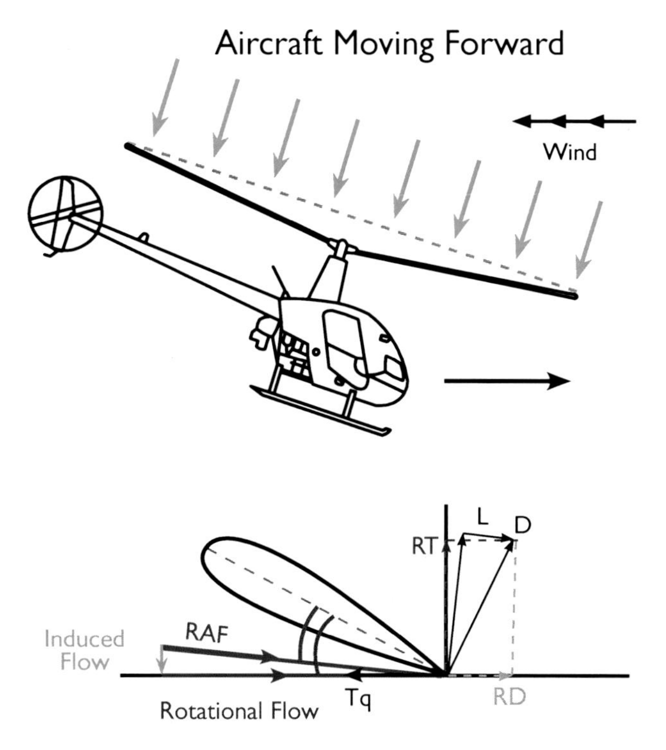

4. Inflow Roll

The fact that you are going forward means that you have tilted the disc forward. Now the airflow across the disc does indeed flow across the disc at the front reducing the induced flow and giving more lift, as above. However the disc is tilted up at the back, therefore this "wind effect" hits that part of the disc and cannot go anywhere but through it, thereby increasing the induced flow. Following the argument above, more induced flow means less lift. So this means more lift at the front of the disc, and less at the back, so where does the roll come in?

(extreme attitude for illustrative purposes only) :

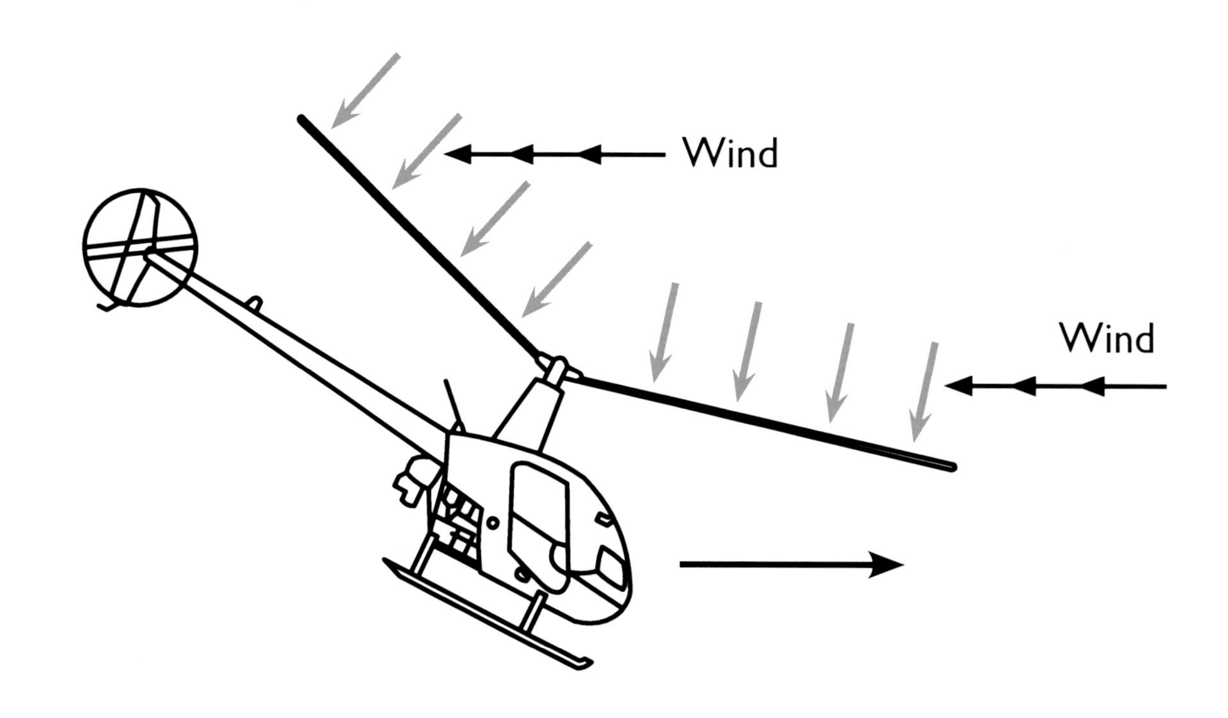

Back of Disc

RT
L
D
RAF
Induced Flow
Rotational Flow
Tq
RD

In the Hover
Original Amount of Induced Flow

Front of Disc

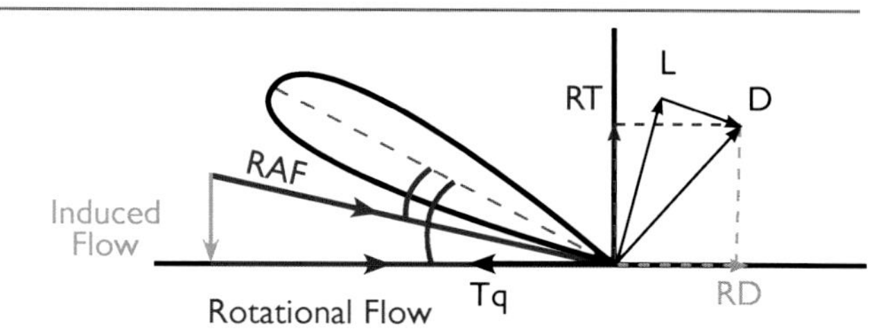

In the Hover
Original Amount of Induced Flow

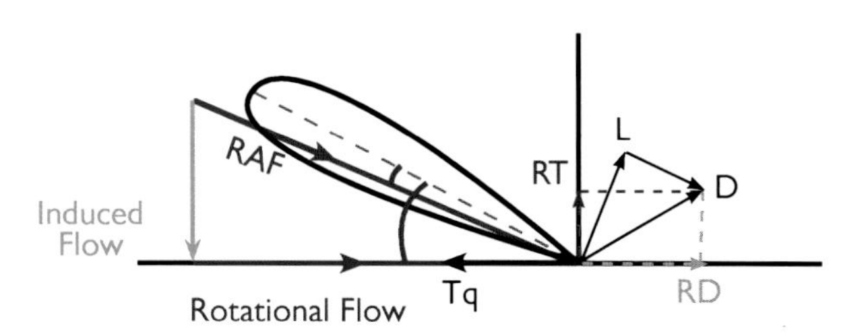

During Transition
More Induced Flow -
Less Lift at Back of Disc

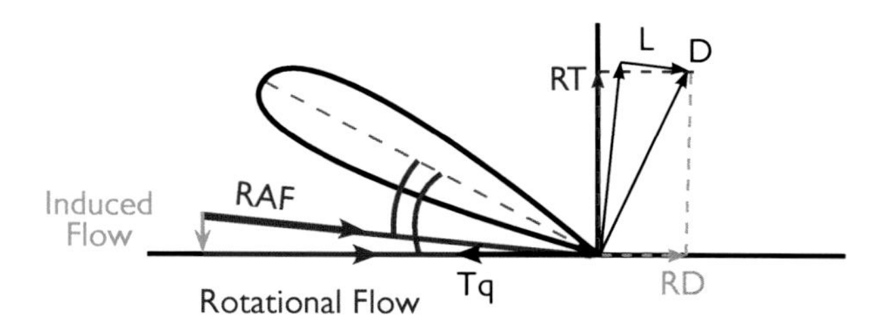

During Transition
Less Induced Flow -
More Lift at Back of Disc

Well, due to precession (if you don't know what this is please see appendix 2) the effect takes place 90° further round the disc in the direction of rotation. So the aircraft will tend to roll towards the advancing side of the disc. This effect is very marked in the Enstrom, less so in the Robinson.

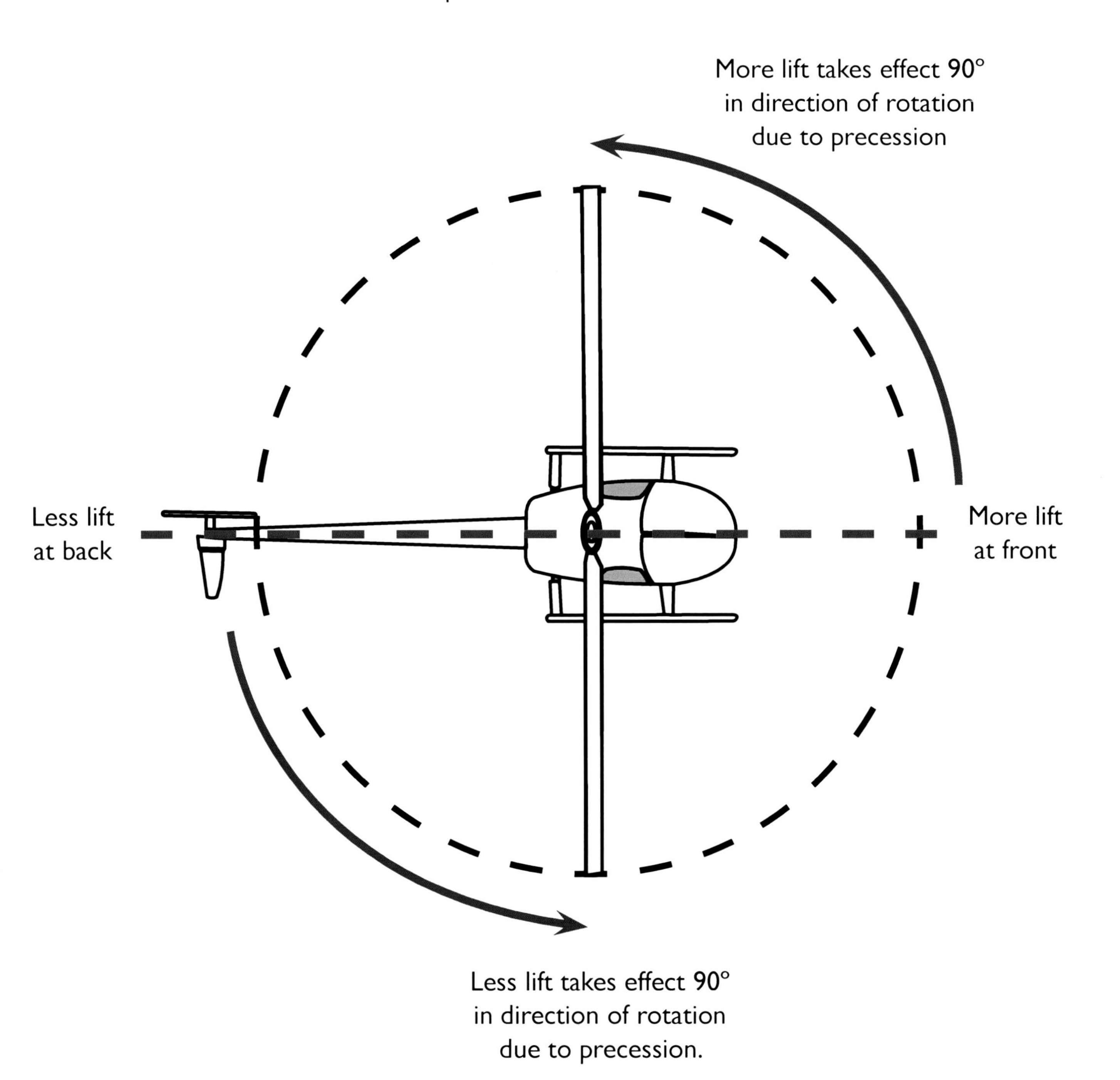

It is possible to over-pitch a helicopter, and this most often occurs during the transition. If you are pulling full power and you apply more pitch in the rotor blades then they will slow down, but you will not have any power in hand to increase torque to counter the increased rotor drag.

A stage may be reached where, due to the amount of pitch applied by the blades, they slow down quickly; over-pitching. Recovery is by lowering the lever to reduce the pitch on the blades and hence the rotor drag. If you've just done this by transitioning away from the hover, it will mean a fast running landing.

Notes :

In order to stop the helicopter we bring the cyclic rearwards (forwards to go forward, back to go back - remember?). When we do this fairly quickly it is called, not unreasonably, a quickstop, and a number of things happen.

The first thing that happens, of course, is that we slow down. Why? Well, in forward flight there is a horizontal component of Rotor Thrust which is pulling us forward, as per the diagram below. When we flare, this thrust is now reversed and acts the opposite way and slows us down :

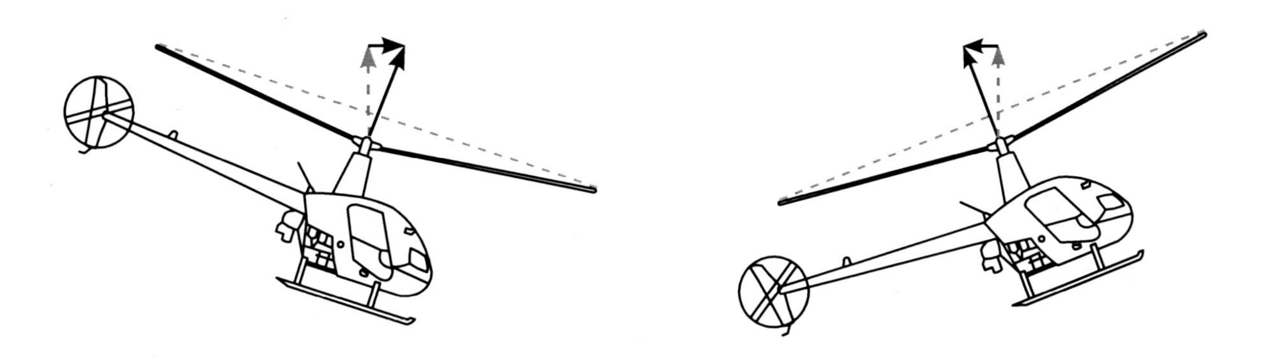

The second thing that happens is that we climb. If you think about it, logically we should actually descend because in tilting the Rotor Thrust we have lost an amount of its vertical component. But we don't, we actually climb. Why?

Well, we still have forward airspeed on, and by tilting the disc backwards we effectively have airflow coming up towards the bottom of the disc, and opposing the induced flow :

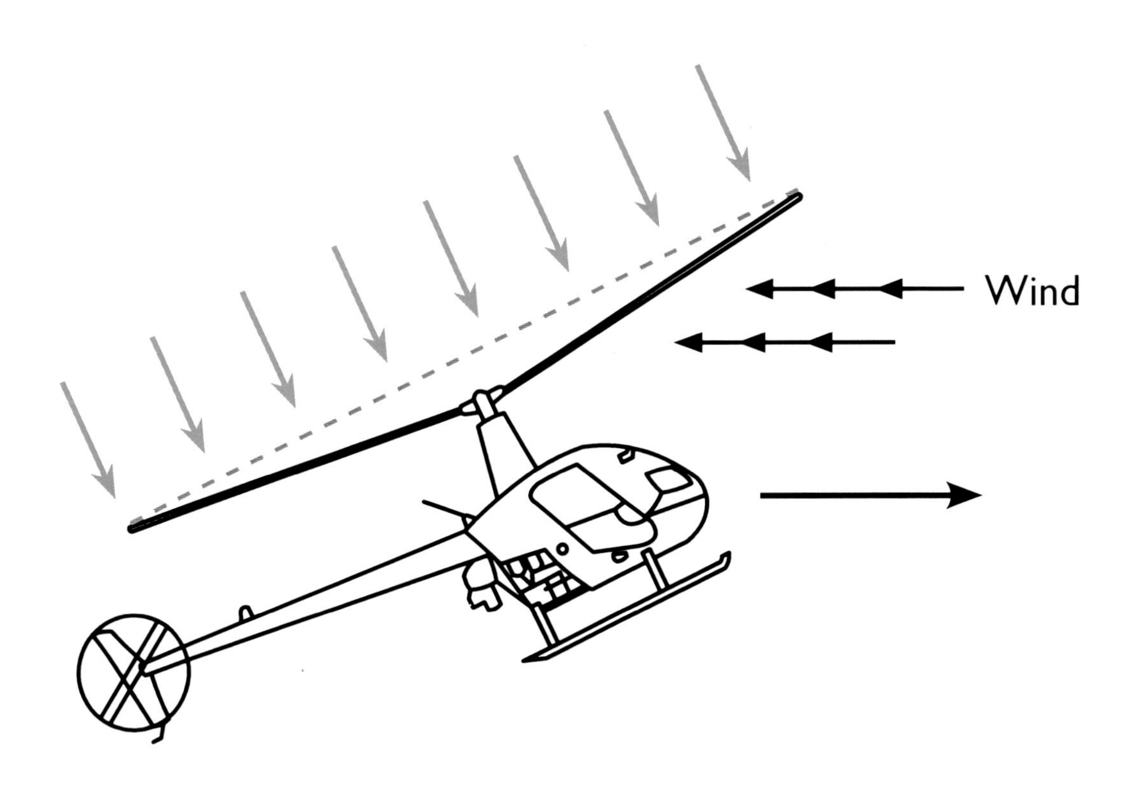

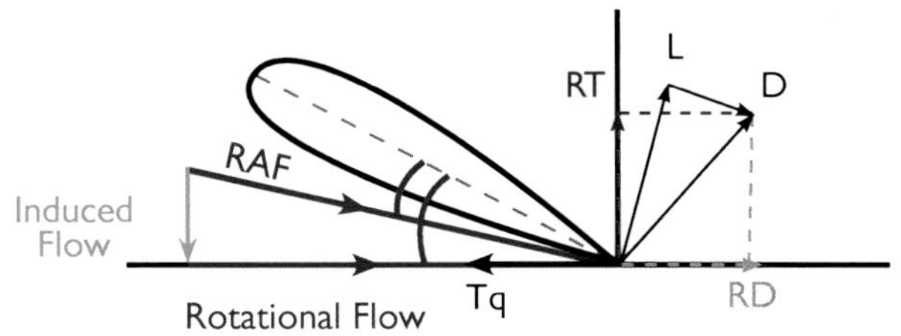

Original Amount of Induced Flow

Less Induced Flow During Flare

Back to the vector diagram. If we reduced the induced flow, then we get (for a given pitch angle) a new relative airflow, and an increased angle of attack. More angle of attack means more lift and we go up.

Another effect of the flare is that the RRPM rise, although this may be masked by a modern correlator or governor. The RRPM rise for two reasons. Referring to the above vector diagrams, because of the reduced induced flow, lift moves towards the axis of rotation and therefore rotor drag is reduced. Also, because we load the disc we also get the coriolis or ice skater effect.

Finally, once we have flared the helicopter, if we hold the cyclic in the same position the nose will continue to pitch up (but once established the disc will flap forward, therefore progressive movement of the cyclic is required to maintain the flared attitude).

If you look at the drawing of a helicopter below, you will see that the rearward component of Rotor Thrust acts above the aircraft's Centre of Gravity. It is therefore trying to pitch the nose up. Meanwhile, Parasite drag is acting rearwards below the C of G and is trying to pitch the nose down. Parasite drag varies as V^3. Therefore as speed reduces, Parasite drag reduces markedly and therefore has less effect in pulling the nose down. The nose will therefore pitch up without any pilot input.

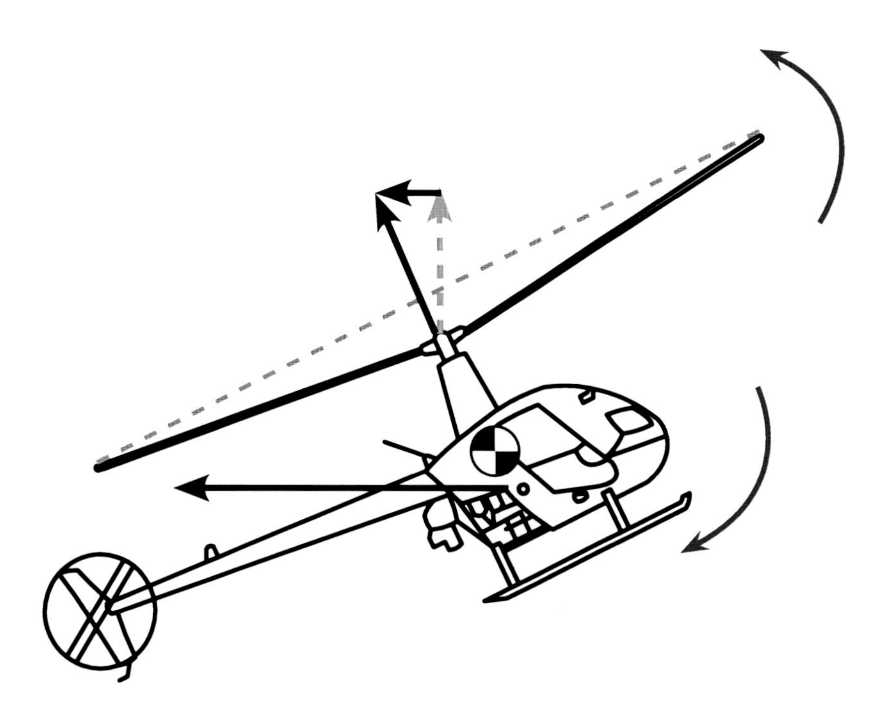

Therefore in a quickstop; we reduce speed; the aircraft climbs; the RRPM increase and the nose pitches up. Your highly qualified instructor will show you how to compensate for these so that you can stop level and without the blades winding themselves off the head!

Notes:

Notes :

You're flying along quite happily when there's a muffled bang; followed by a strange silence from the engine area. Apart from thinking "what the *** was that?" you'll need to get the lever down - quickly - and enter autorotation. Why? Well it's back to the vector diagram again. In normal flight you will recall that Rotor Drag is opposed by engine power (torque). If the engine fails, or we close the throttle, then the blades will slow down under the influence of the Rotor Drag.

Normal Powered Flight

Blades are driven by the engine which provides enough rotor thrust to overcome drag and keep the helicopter flying

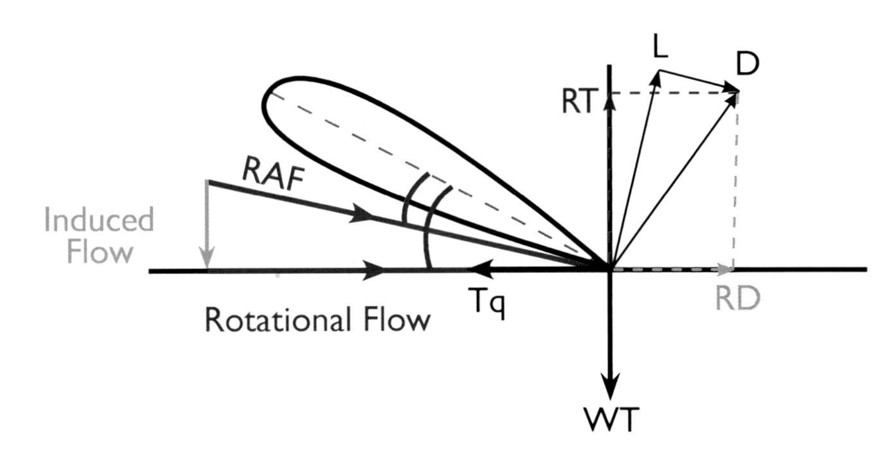

The rate at which the blades slow down will depend on the amount of pitch applied (and hence the amount of Rotor Drag) and also their inertia. High inertia blades slow down relatively slowly; whilst low inertia blades slow down relatively quickly. If the blades slow down too much and get below their critical minimum RRPM they may stall. One of two things may occur; either the blades will rapidly cone up until they clap hands, or one blade will stall first (usually the retreating blade, but this is not "retreating blade stall", which occurs at high speed and normal RRPM) which causes the disc to become unstable and the retreating blade to descend and chop the tail off. The outcome of either of these events is usually fatal for all on board. But lets look at the bright side of life and see what can be done to avoid such an eventuality. Initially we lower the lever to minimum pitch :

Initial Entry

Reduces rotor drag but also reduces rotor thrust

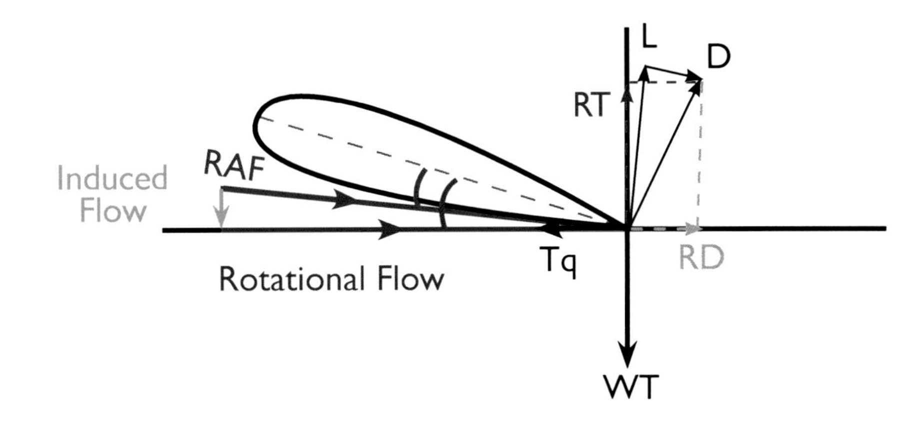

This reduces Rotor Drag so the blades slow down less quickly. However, it also reduces Rotor Thrust. This now becomes less than Weight and the helicopter starts to descend. Because the helicopter is now descending the airflow comes from below, a Rate of Descent flow. In the diagram below this has been exaggerated for illustrative purposes, but if you follow the vector diagram through you will see that Rotor Drag now acts on the opposite side of the Axis of Rotation to that which it did originally. It acts on the side that Engine Power did, in fact it becomes a power equivilant and is an aerodynamic force driving the blades.

Established Autorotaion

Rotor drag moves ahead of the axis of rotation to provide a power equivilant to angle of attack to drive the blades

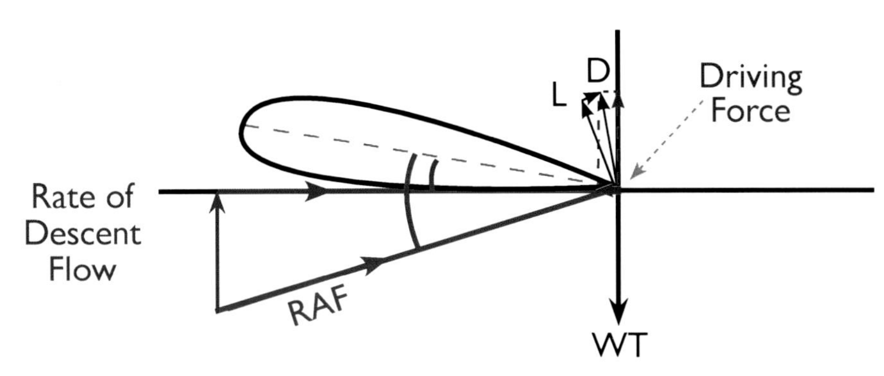

How are the RRPM controlled in autorotation? It gets just a little complicated here, so pay attention and read slowly please. For the following diagrams I have ignored washout as it makes it easier to illustrate, but it doesn't alter the aerodynamics. Let's take a blade :

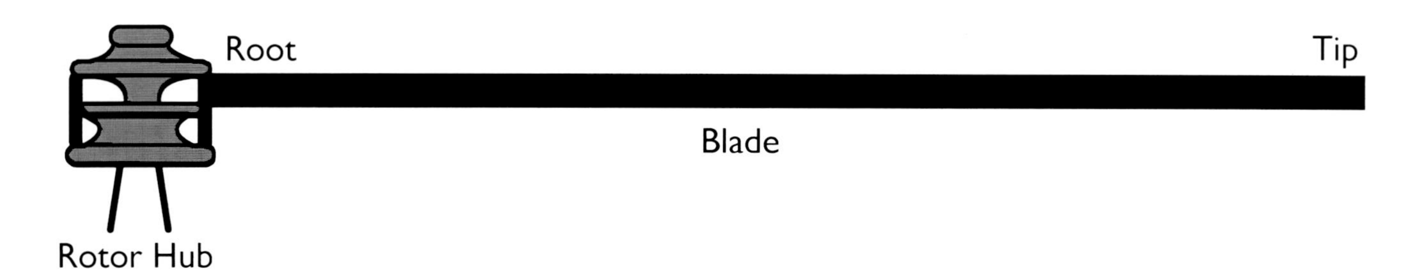

Now let's construct three vector diagrams along the blade. As I explained earlier, because we are going down, there will be a rate of descent flow :

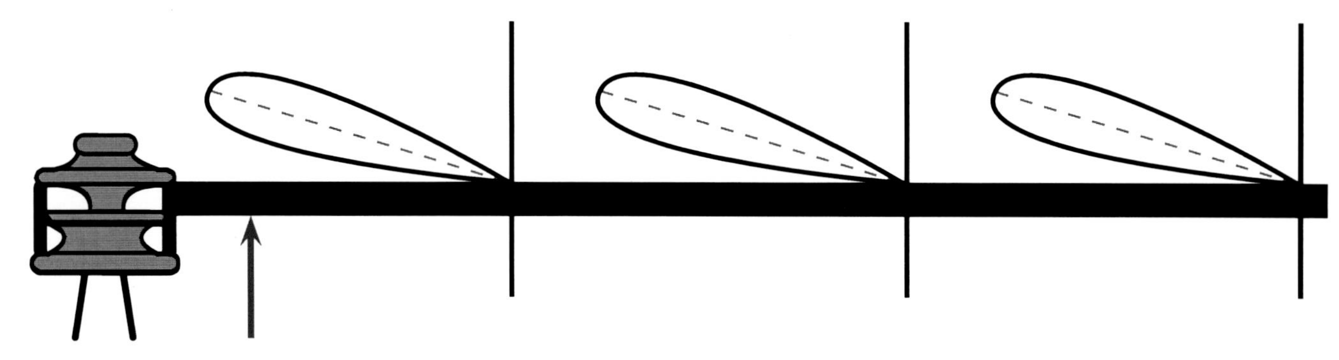

This gives the following relative air flows :

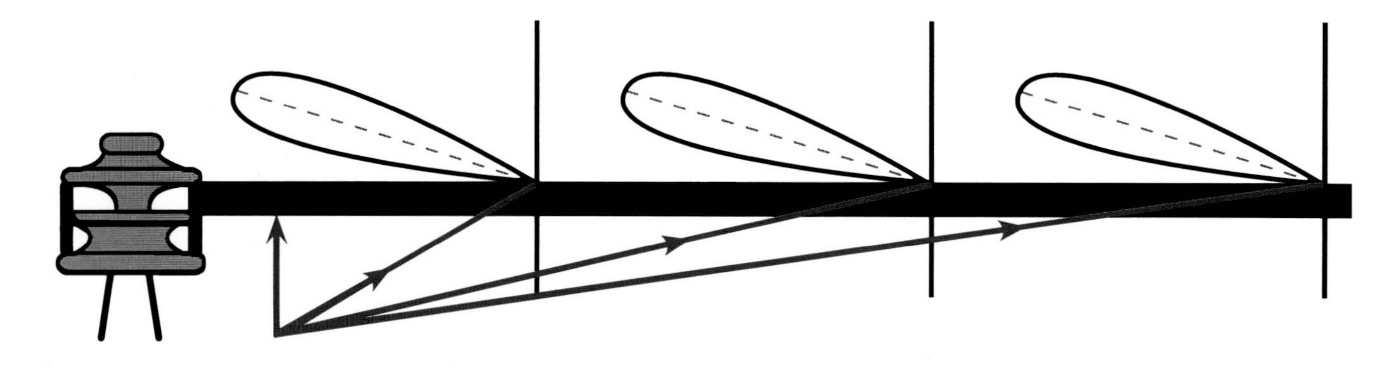

and the following vector diagrams :

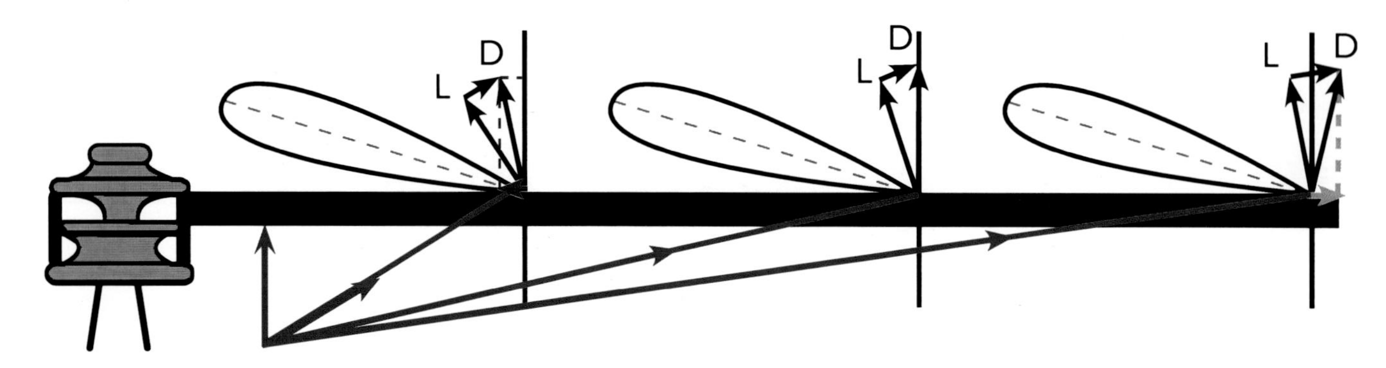

You will see that at the tip we have something approaching a normal vector diagram. Here the total reaction is behind the axis of rotation, trying to slow the blade down. At the middle section illustrated, total reaction is along the axis of rotation and is neither driving nor dragging. At the section drawn closest to the root, the total reaction is ahead of the axis of rotation, driving the blades.

Right at the blade root itself there is an angle of attack so great that this blade section is probably stalled (and when an aerofoil is stalled, the airflow breaks away from it and lift is markedly reduced). This, however, doesn't help us with an explanation of autorotation, so I have ignored it.

So long as the driving section is bigger than the dragging section, the blades will continue to rotate and we float gently towards the ground for a graceful engine off landing. We can alter the RRPM in the autorotation by raising and lowering the lever to alter the pitch angle of the blade. If we raise the lever and increase the pitch angle, the section of the blade at the "neutral drive" point, now becomes a dragging section as the total reaction will move behind the axis of rotation, and vice versa.

Of course, an autorotation is not just an emergency descent, but a perfectly normal way of descending a helicopter quickly. Most people who don't fly helicopters think that if you disconnect the engine from the blades or the engine fails you plummet to earth and crash. Now you know differently, so amaze your friends and stun your neighbours...

The Avoid Curve
For every helicopter there is an avoid curve diagram included in the pilots notes. This shows two areas, one at low airspeed and one at high airspeed, when a pilot may have difficulty in entering an autorotation and completing a successful engine-off landing in the event of engine failure. Two points about this curve. Firstly it is only a guide derived from test flights in the best conditions. Secondly, it is not a "never enter curve" but one where it is best to avoid continuous operations. If you are aware that you are flying in the avoid curve, then you are better prepared if the worst comes to the worst.

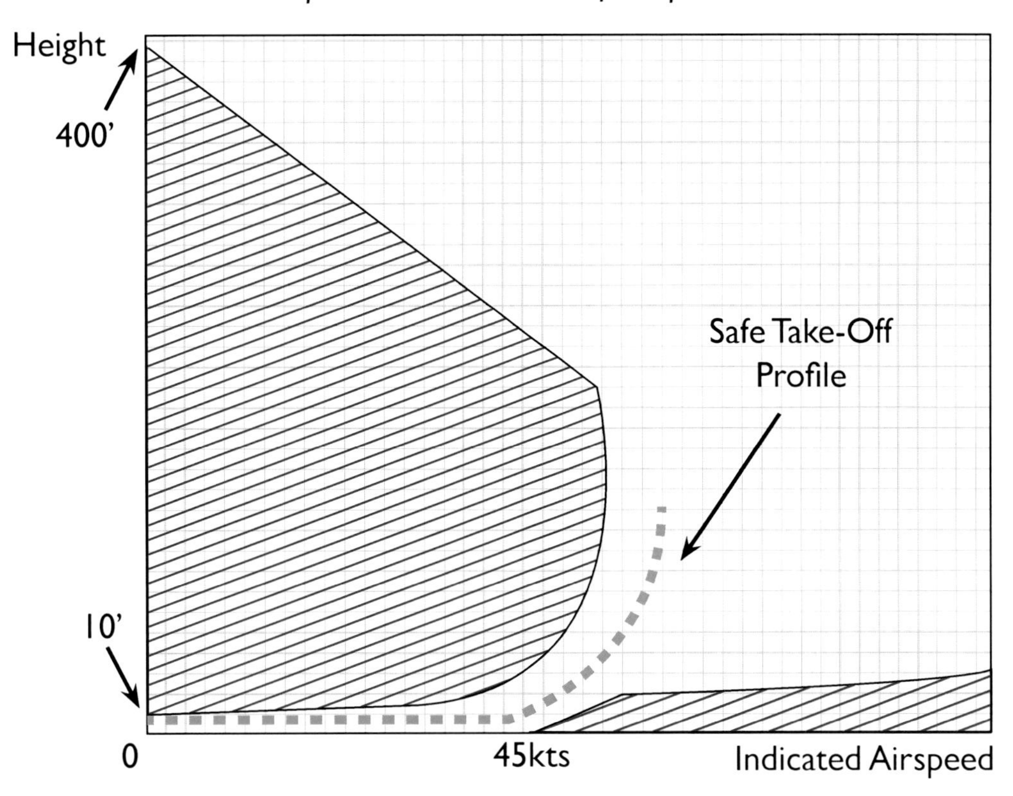

Notes :

There is a state of flight, generally best avoided, called Vortex Ring. Well, anyway, that's what it's usually called in the UK, although in the U.S. it's generally referred to as Settling with Power; which is probably a better descriptive title.

Let's take a helicopter flying along. It will have induced flow through disc :

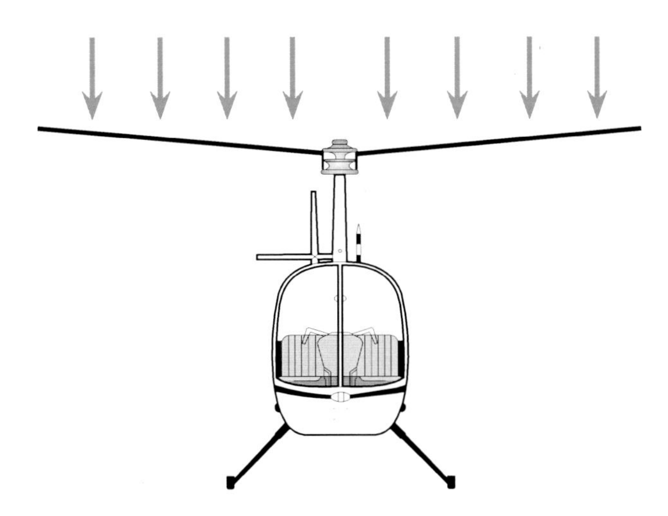

Now, if the helicopter starts to descend, it will experience a Rate of Descent flow which will oppose the induced flow :

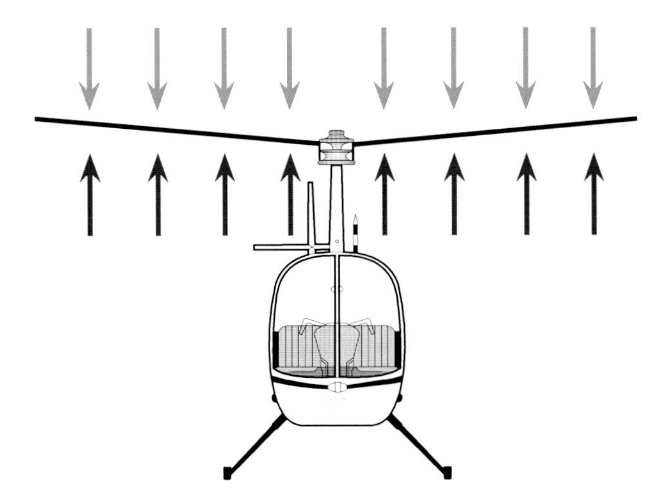

We will get Vortex Ring when we get a lot of Induced Flow being opposed by a lot of Rate of Descent Flow (I'll explain how and why in a minute).

We know that as we increase speed, Induced Flow reduces. Therefore to get a lot of Induced Flow we need to be going slowly; a generally accepted figure is less than 30 kts (IAS). To get a reasonable amount of Rate of Descent Flow we need to be going down at a reasonable rate; a generally accepted figure for this is in excess of 300 ft/min.

Therefore we now have two of the requirements for Vortex Ring. The third one is power applied. If you recall from the explanation of autorotations there was no induced flow as all the induced flow came from below. Therefore we cannot get Vortex Ring whilst actually in autorotation. So, to get Vortex Ring we need :

1. Low IAS (less than 30 kts)
2. High ROD (more than 300 ft/min)
3. Power applied

So, what happens, to actually give us Vortex Ring? Well, let's look at two points on a blade; the tip and the root. Firstly, our standard vector diagram for each of these points (we only need to work on the left hand side of the vector diagram) :

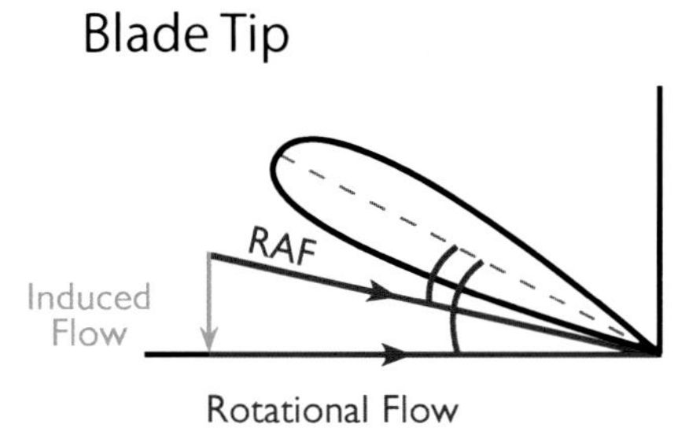

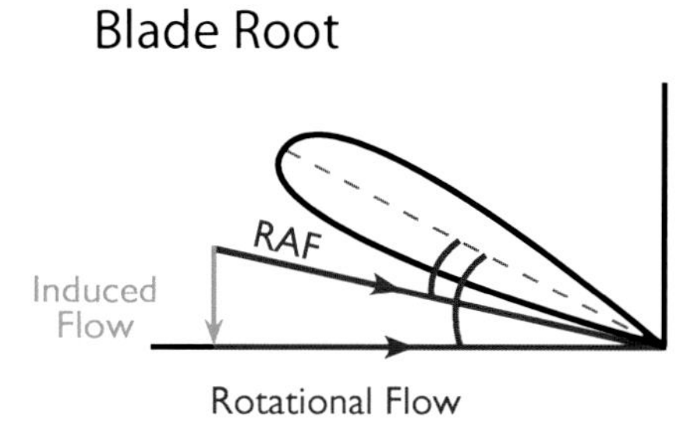

Lets now have the helicopter descending and see what happens.

At the tip, airflow from below tries to escape round the tip but then gets sucked back in, thereby increasing the Induced Flow. We know by now that increased Induced Flow means a smaller angle of attack and less lift :

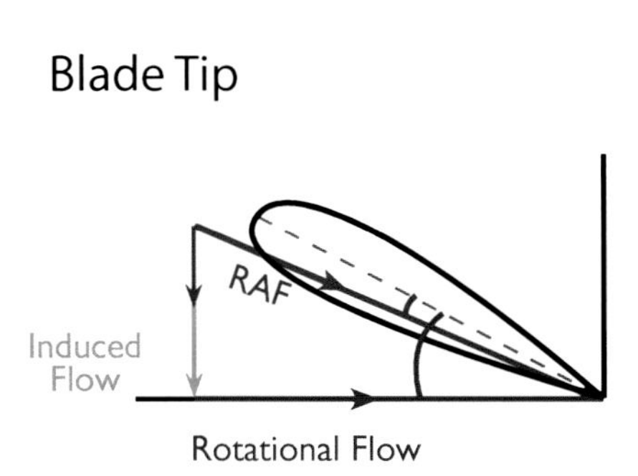

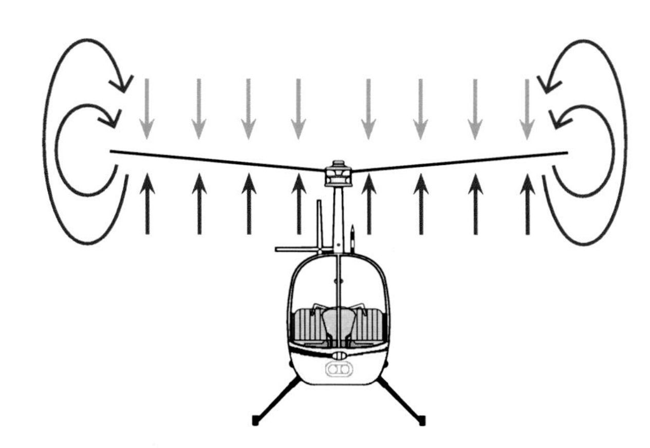

Therefore, the rate of descent of the helicopter increases, making the situation worse. The helicopter is, in fact, settling with power.

Now let's look at what happens at the root. Here the Rate of Descent Flow has no option but to go through the disc. All the flow will be from below and the blade will experience a very high angle of attack, probably well in excess of the 15° - 17° that an aerofoil normally stalls at :

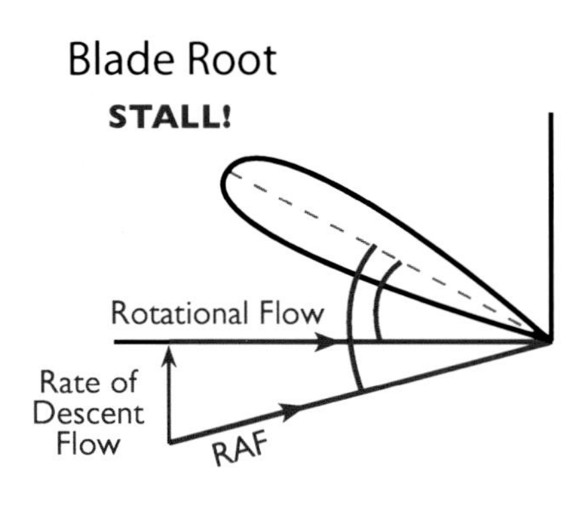

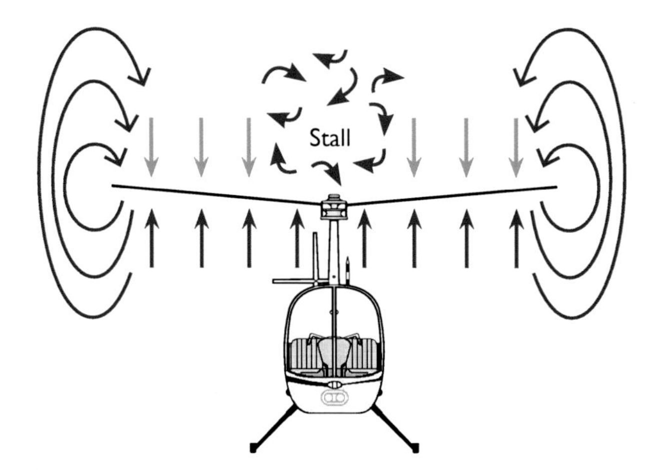

When an aerofoil stalls it looses lift so the helicopter's Rate of Descent will increase again, making the situation worse still.

Due to the airflow breaking away from the blade we will experience stick shake and random yaw.

So the symptoms of Vortex Ring are :

1. An increase in ROD
2. Stick shake and random yaw

When can we get the conditions conductive to Vortex Ring? Well, typically but not exclusively :

During a normal approach
During a steep approach
On a vertical descent
On recovery from autorotation
During a quickstop
During a downwind approach (if you are foolish enough to attempt such a thing)

Recovery? Well, the best recovery is not to get into Vortex Ring in the first place! If you are fully aware of the conditions necessary for it to develop, you can avoid them. This is definitely worth doing when you consider - that in a fully developed Vortex Ring - you could have a rate of descent of several hundred feet per minute, and most of the situations where it occurs you will be fairly close to the ground.

To recover you need to get rid of any one of the three conditions necessary for Vortex Ring. So you could, for example, enter autorotation. However, given that you will be fairly close to the ground and descending rapidly this is probably not going to be favourite. An alternative, and more favourable way would be to increase speed to above 30 kts and then increase power to climb away.

Whilst in training you will do this gently; in the real situation you will want to increase speed to above 30 kts then increase power rapidly and at the same time raise the nose to get away from the ground / trees / buildings which will be approaching. Establish a climb before taking a deep breath and taking stock of the situation. Believe me. Been there, done that.

Whatever you do, don't raise the lever before increasing the airspeed as you will only make the stall worse.

Notes :

When you move a body through the air, a resistance to that movement is generated (drag). A helicopter generates three kinds of drag.

1. Rotor Profile Drag

This is drag generated by the rotor (plus all the ancillary equipment driven by the main rotor gearbox) at minimum pitch. Ancillary equipment includes the tail rotor. The combined graph for rotor profile drag looks like this :

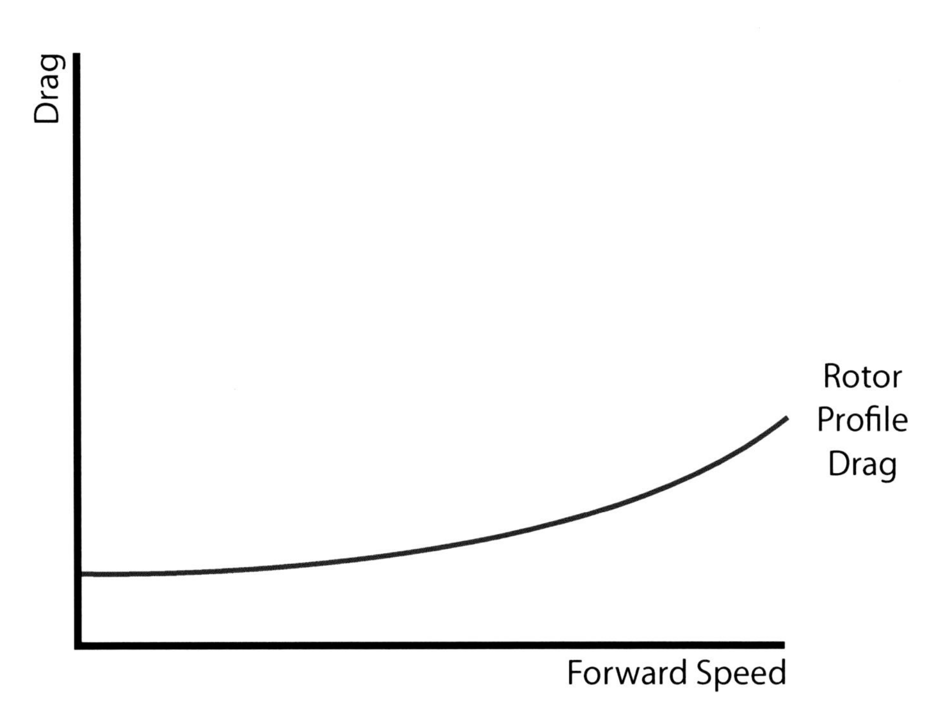

2. Induced Drag

Increased drag generated by the increase in induced flow as we increase pitch is called Induced Drag. We know that as we increase speed Induced Flow reduces, therefore Induced Drag reduces also. The graph for Induced Drag looks like this :

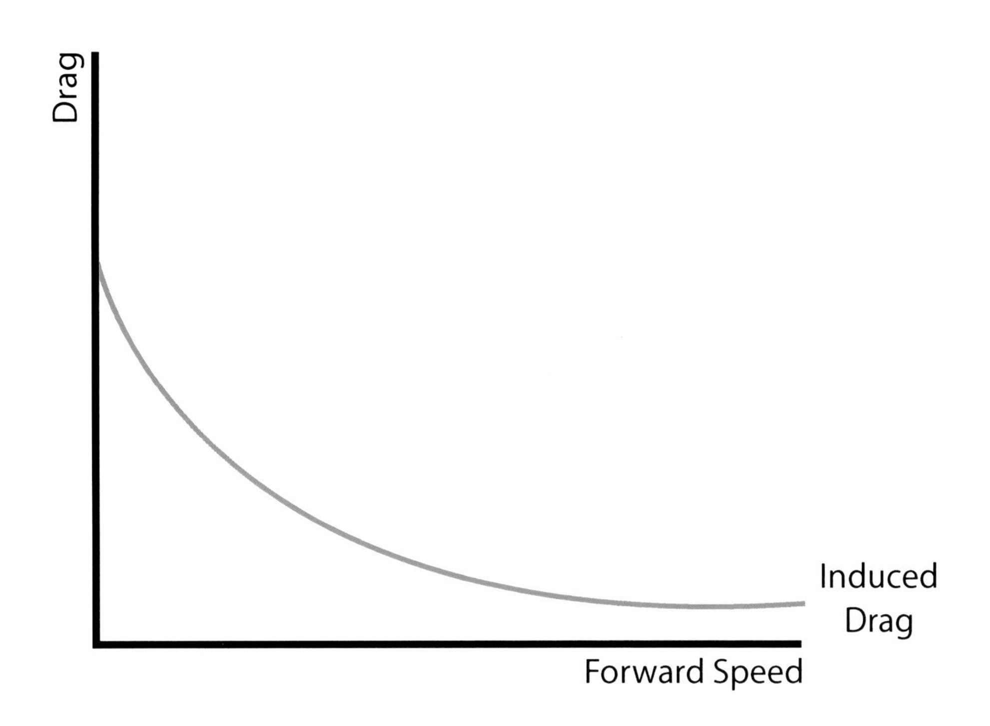

3. Parasite Drag

As speed is increased, the drag generated by the fuselage, skids, fairings etc. increases. Drag generated by these things is called Parasite Drag and varies in proportion to speed as V^3.

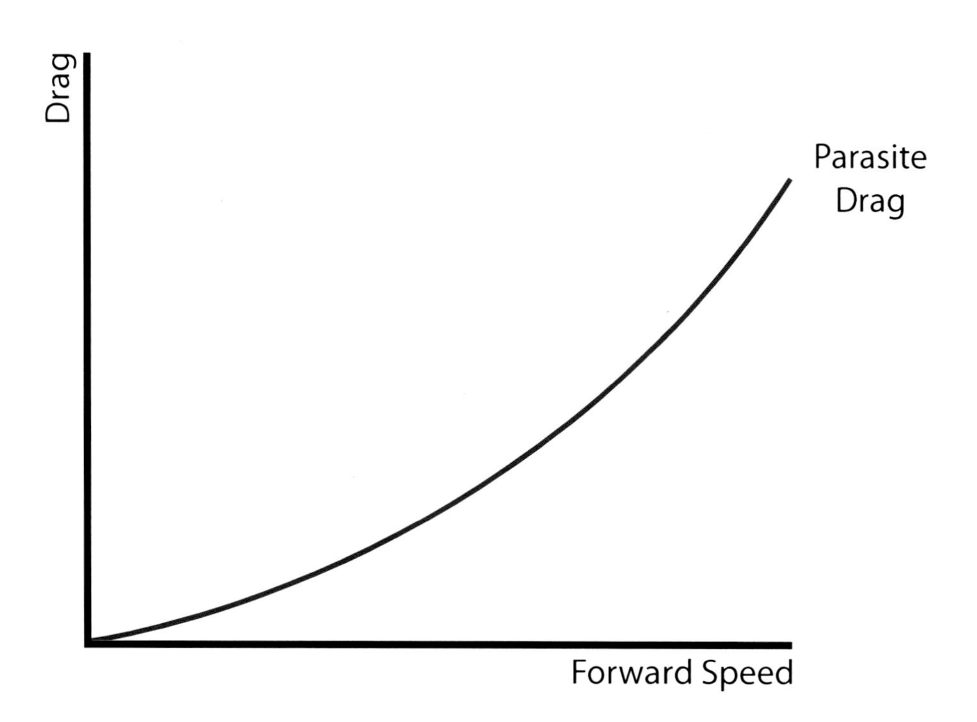

If we put these three types of drag onto one graph we can also add them up to give us a total drag curve - I say add them up, but of course we've kept this really simple by not putting any values on either axis. We simply say that this is roughly the shape of the appropriate curve.

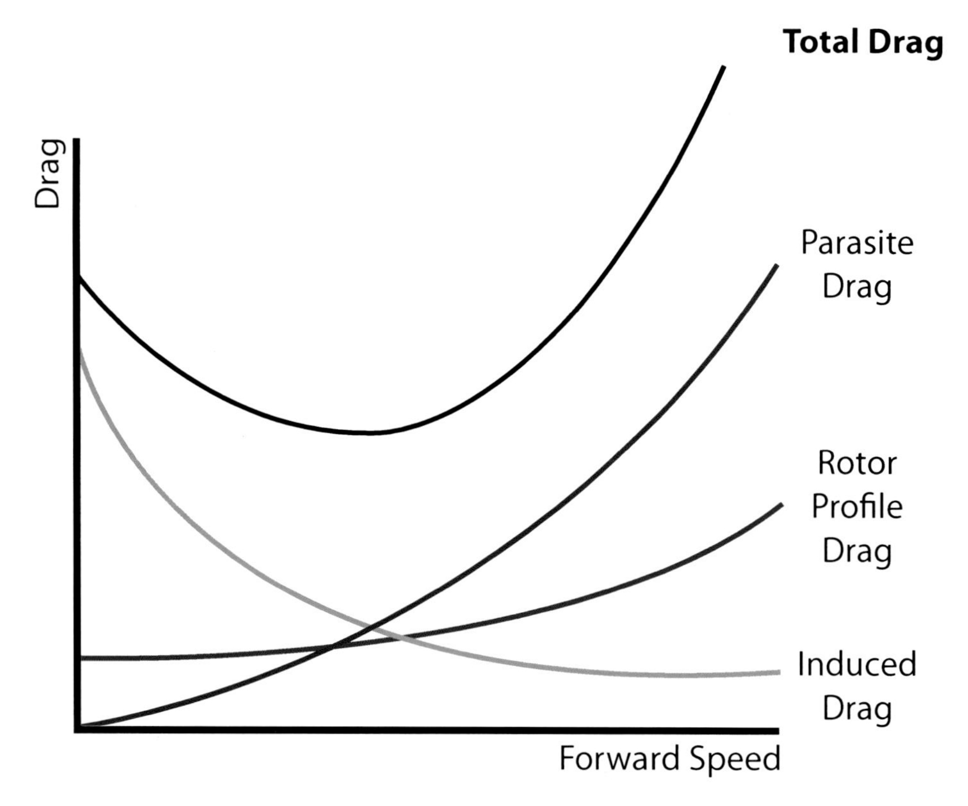

Now if drag is slowing us down, then we need something to overcome this. This something is power. So we can now substitute power for drag on the vertical axis of the graph to give us a Power Required graph :

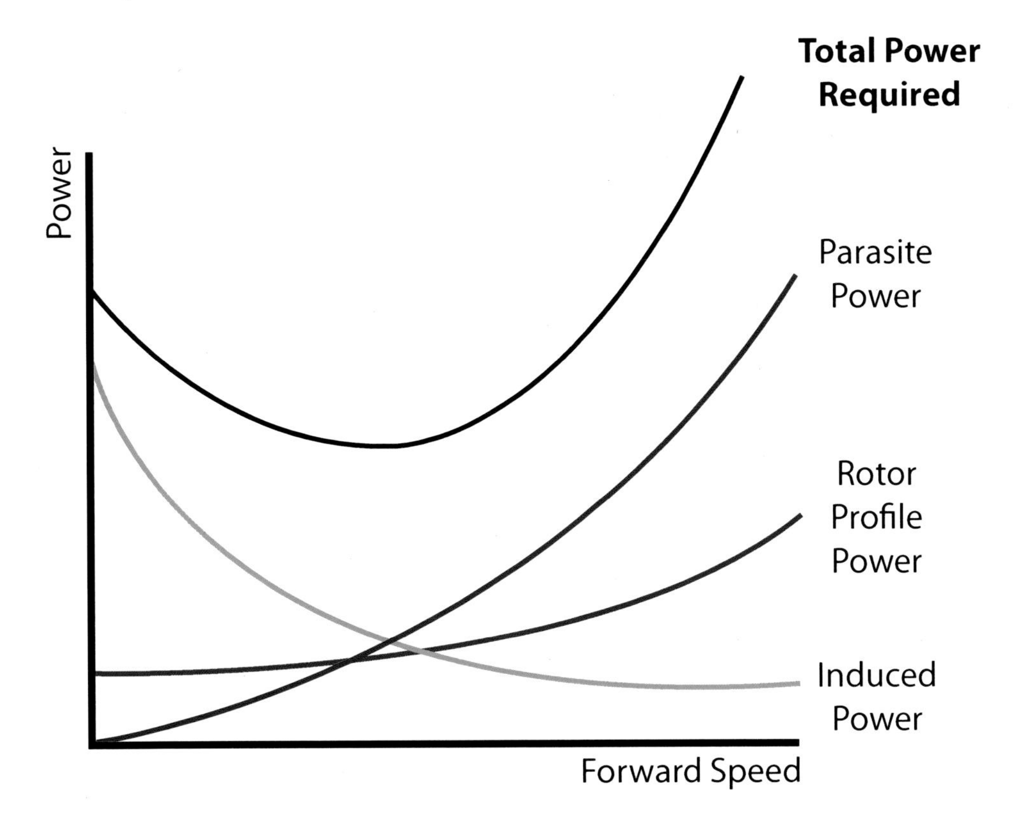

For a piston engined helicopter the power available from the engine is constant with speed, so we add this to the graph and now it is almost complete :

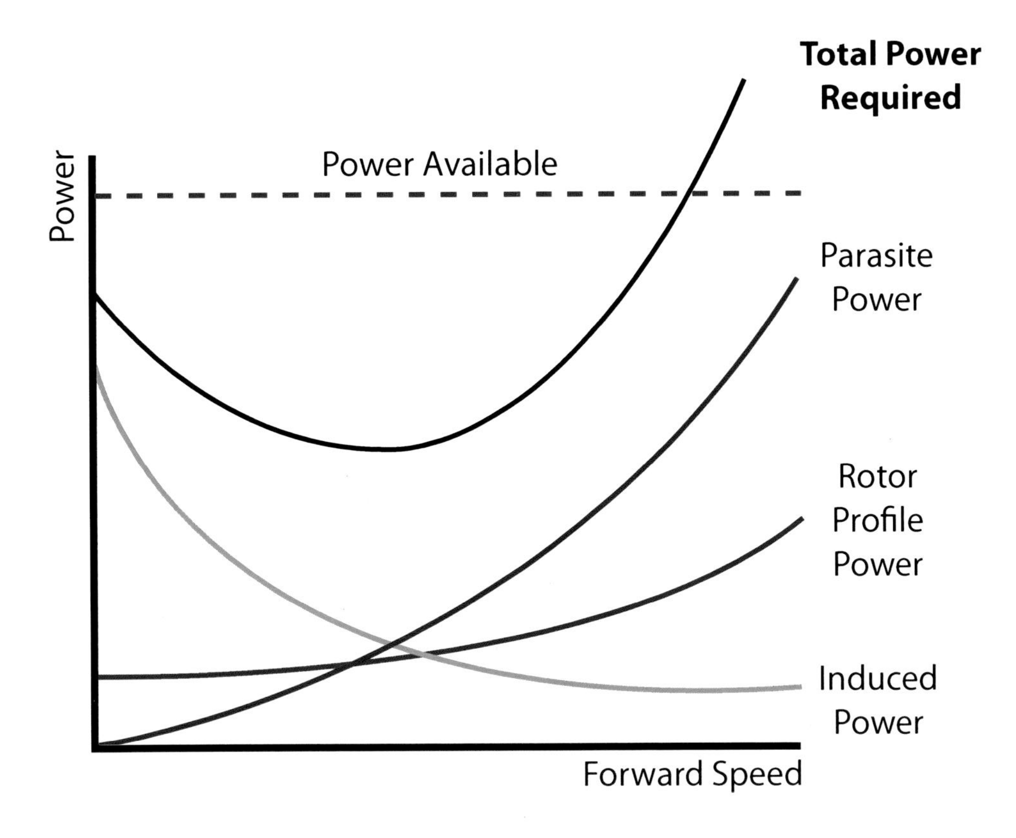

From this graph we can establish a number of useful points :

1. Maximum Straight and Level Speed

This will be where the total power required curve meets the power available curve; to go any faster will require more power which simply isn't there.

2. Endurance Speed

This will be where we are using the minimum amount of power (and therefore fuel) and can therefore stay airborne for the longest time. This speed can be found at the bottom of the Power Required Curve.

3. Best Rate of Climb Speed

This will be where we have the greatest power margin (difference between power required and power available) and is at the same point as our endurance speed is.

4. Range Speed

This is a tangent from the origin of the graph to the power required graph. i.e. the best power required / airspeed ratio.

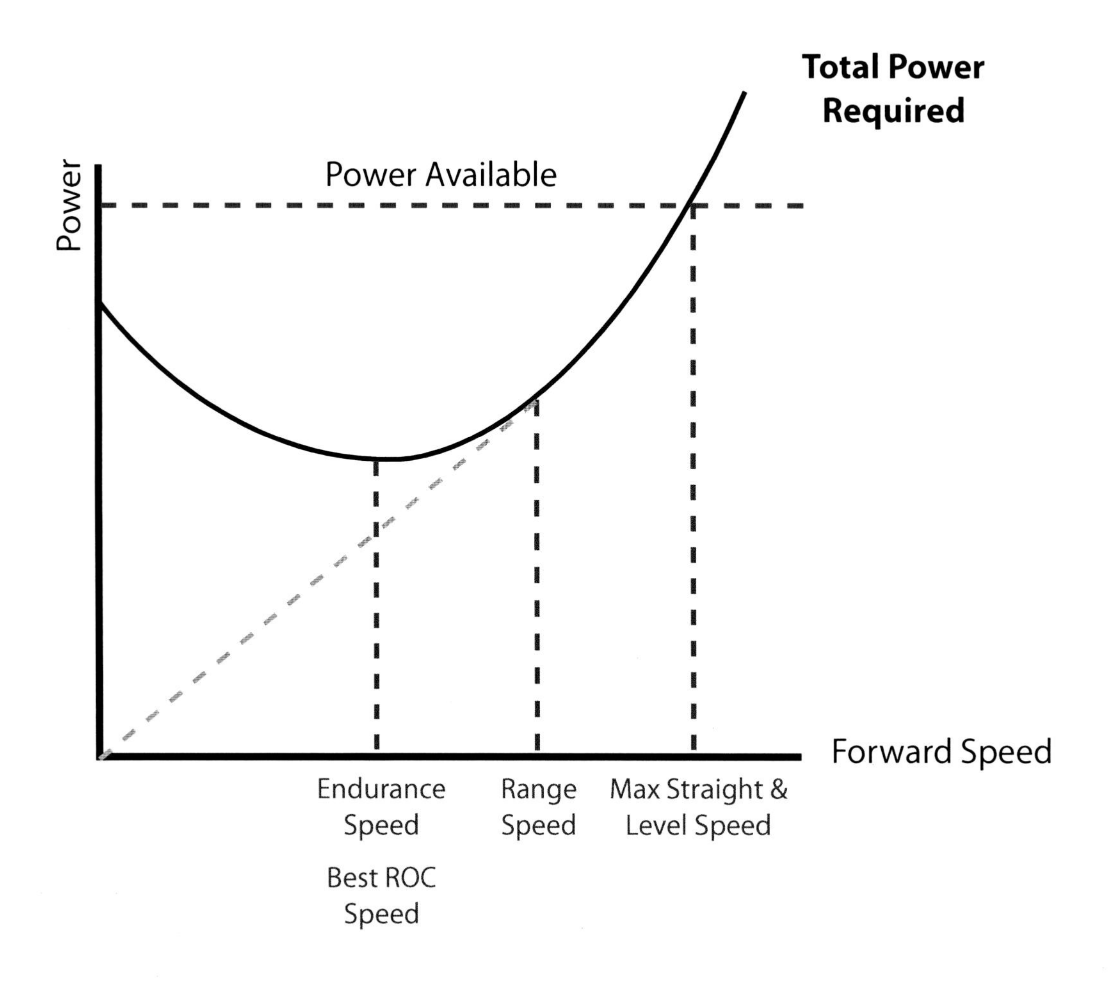

So, what good is all of this to us? Well call me old fashioned if you will, but when operating a helicopter it's always nice to know what power we have in hand.

Our power available may be limited. This could be due to operating at high density altitudes and/or at high ambient temperatures, or an engine that has a technical problem (a fouled spark plug or magneto problem), or simply an engine that is showing signs of age.

Our power required may be higher than estimated or expected. This could be due to an increase in our maximum all up weight (the mate you take flying is "mistaken" about his / her weight).

Whilst the entire range of the power available / power required graphs will be of interest to us, the area around the left hand side, where the speed is at or near zero and the power available and power required are in close proximity will be of particular interest.

So, let's expand that part of the graph and also modify the power required to take account of ground effect. You will recall, I hope, that as we move off the ground cushion we initially need more power before we get translational lift and can reduce power. We can represent this on the graph :

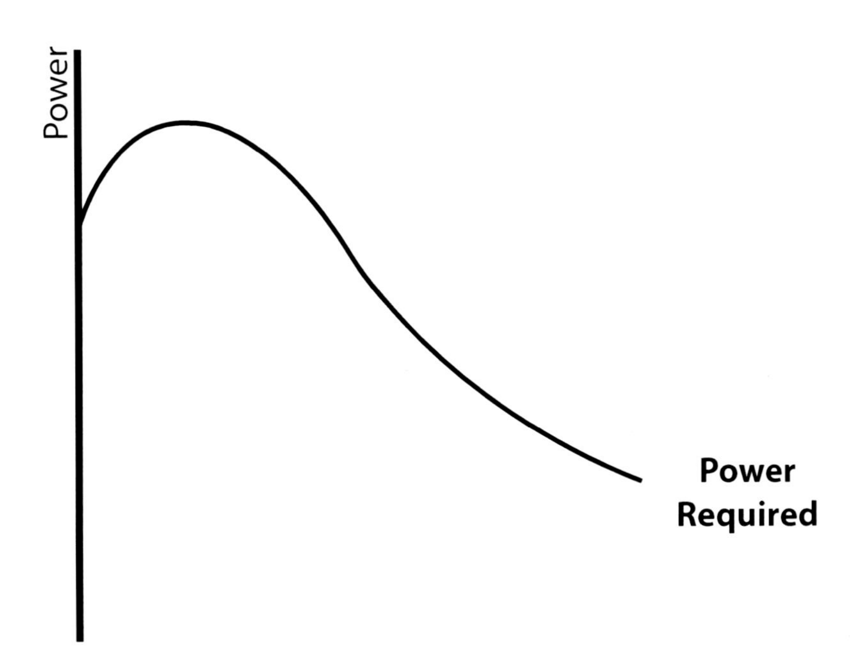

Now, if the power available reduces or the power required increases, then the two graphs cross. In an extreme case we will not have enough power to hover in ground effect, let alone out of it. In this case we will not be able to get airborne until we reach a speed where power required becomes less than power available; we will have to do a running take-off or running landing :

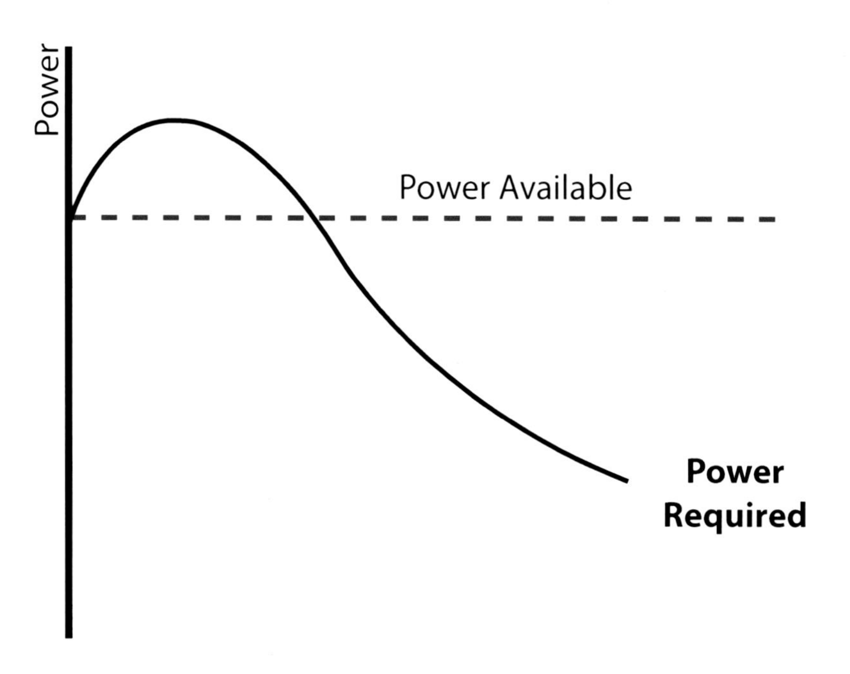

If we have slightly more power available we may be able to get into the hover, but will run out of power when we start to transition forward. In this case we will need to take off by taking the ground cushion with us (a cushion creep take-off) or landing without coming to a hover (a zero speed landing) :

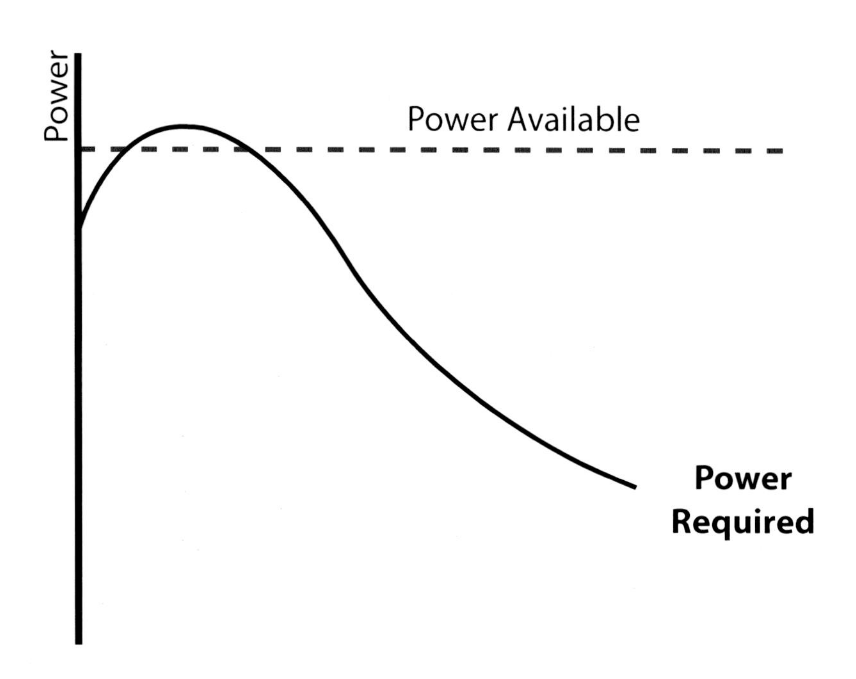

Finally, when operating with limited power, the aircraft must have forward speed in order to climb. When we had lots of power available we had a power margin available at zero speed, so that would have been our best angle of climb speed. To find our best angle of climb speed, when power is limited, we draw a line from where the power available meets the vertical axis of the graph tangentially to the power curve :

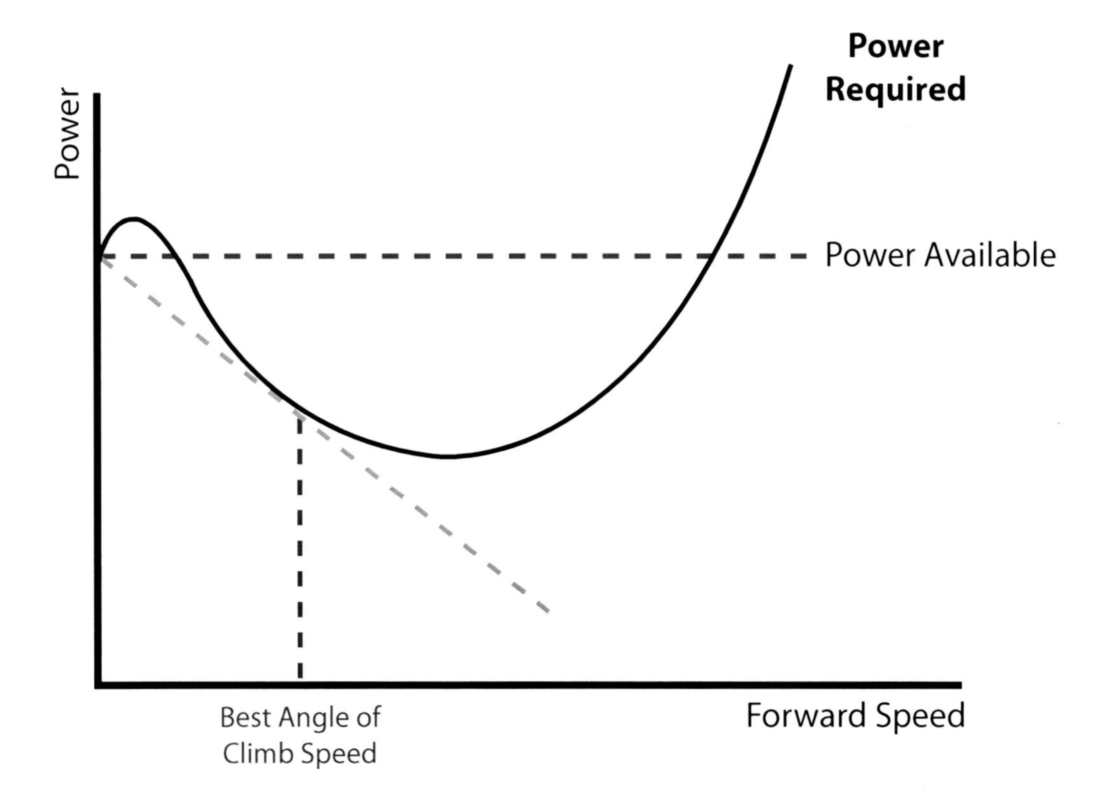

Notes :

There are a number of aspects to helicopter aerodynamics which do not fit neatly into the chapters before, so I've heaped them into this one.

Flapping To Equality

We almost covered this during flapback, but veered away to concentrated on what was happening to the disc. So, now lets look at each individual blade.

On the advancing side of the disc, we know that the blade will have more lift and will therefore want to flap up because it has more lift due to the increase in V in the lift formula (Vr + Vw remember?).

Meanwhile, by the same argument, the retreating blade has less lift. Therefore, logically, the helicopter should roll left, but is doesn't. Why not?

On the advancing side, as the blade flaps up it gets more induced flow by virtue of its upward movement. Put your hand straight in front of you. Move it quickly upwards and you'll see what I mean. If it gets more induced flow, then we know from the Vector Diagram that the angle of attack will reduce and therefore reduce the lift.

Meanwhile, on the retreating side the opposite happens, i.e. the blade flaps down. There is an upward flow of air which reduces the induced flow thereby increasing lift.

So, the blades have flapped in order to equalise the lift across the disc; they have Flapped to Equality.

Phase Lag

Phase Lag is the angular difference (usually 90°) between where the blade has its maximum rate of flapping, and the point where it reaches its highest or lowest position.

If you recall Flapback, the advancing blade was at its maximum flapping at the 90° position and then reached a high point at the forward (360° position), whilst the retreating blade did the opposite.

Advance Angle

To change the pitch on blades, you need to exercise leverage on them. For this reason you cannot position the pitch operating arms directly below the blades, but a little way from them.

The amount by which the pitch operating arms are positioned ahead of the blades is called Advanced Angle.

Loss of Tail Rotor Effectiveness (LTE)

LTE can happen to any single rotor helicopter. It is not a failure of the tail rotor, and neither is it a stall of the tail rotor as such, although it may give the appearance of being one of these because it results in an uncommanded, rapid and increasing yaw. This is usually, but not exclusively, in the opposite direction to which the blades turn.

We know that we use our pedals to maintain directional control by generating thrust from the tail rotor. The wind can cause variations when we are operating at the edge of the low speed flight envelope. They can lead to an uncommanded yaw which in the cockpit we feel as a loss of effectiveness of the tail rotor.

LTE can occur in any low speed high power environment. However, when operating out of ground effect we will have a higher pitch setting which will make us further susceptible, as will carrying out a right turn.

For a helicopter with blades rotating anti-clockwise the critical wind directions are from the left or from the tail.

Recovery is initially to apply full opposite pedal - to the pedal stop if necessary. At the same time increase forward speed to get out of the low speed envelope, and lower the collective which will reduce both the yaw rate and amount of pitch on the tail rotor.

Static Rollover

This is simply when you try and land a helicopter on a slope which is too steep for it. The centre of gravity moves outside of the skids and rolls the aircraft over :

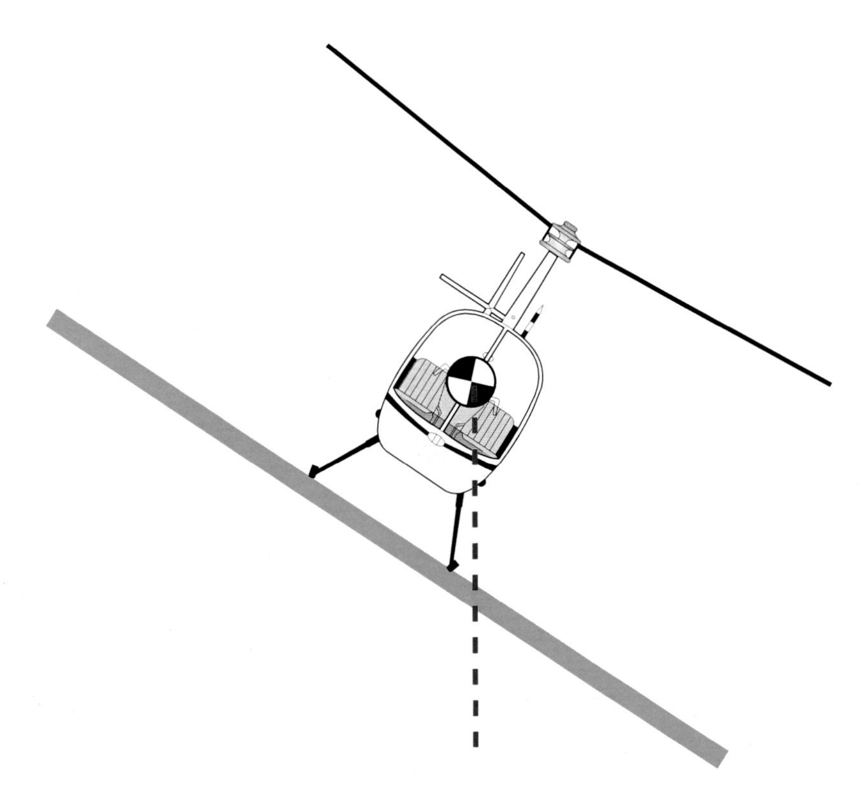

Most helicopter flight manuals do not publish "limits" for slope landings as it is considered that the outcome of a slope landing is a function of pilot skill and not of aircraft design.

Dynamic Rollover

As its name implies, Dynamic Rollover is associated with movement. It is caused by angular velocity of the helicopter mass about a skid, which is in contact with the ground. This can occur on take-off or landing, and on flat or sloping ground.

However, this is well illustrated by considering a helicopter with a relatively high Centre of Gravity (C of G) lifting off and for whatever reason (a skid sticking, incorrect cyclic position relative to the C of G or wind, for example) developing a roll.

To control this may require more angular momentum from the cyclic than it was designed for. Therefore, applying opposite cyclic may not be enough to stop the roll once it has reached a critical rate.

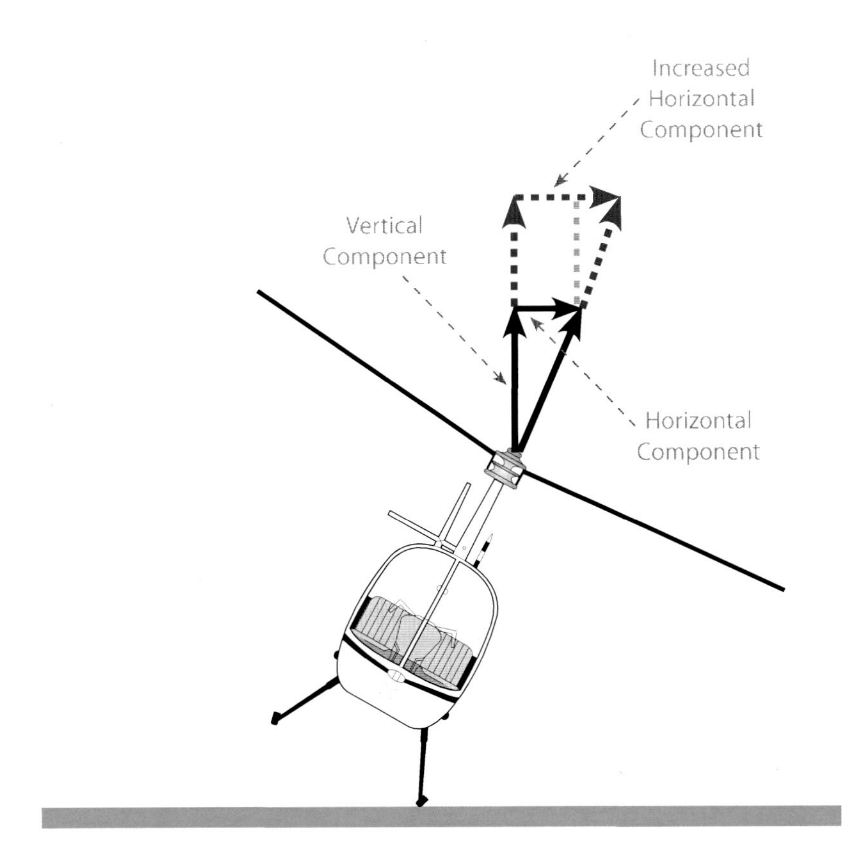

This can be further exacerbated by applying collective pitch in order to try and "pull" the helicopter off the ground. In this case as well; as increasing the vertical component of rotor thrust, increasing the lever increases the horizontal component and simply pulls the aircraft over, not off, the ground.

Notes :

Fixed wing aircraft have a range of top speeds from the slowest (microlights etc.) at approx. 50 kts to the fastest (Concorde) at Mach 2 (approximately 1,323 kts). However, the range of maximum speed for helicopters only varies from approximately 70 kts to around 250 kts. Why is this? Well, as with most things, there are a number of reasons :

1. Forward Cyclic

As we increase speed, we know that the disc flaps back. To overcome this, we need to move the cyclic forward. The disc flaps back again and we move the cyclic forward again, and so on. There comes a point when you cannot move the cyclic any further forward. Flapback and cyclic controls will always (well, until some genius finds a way around it) be a limit to the forward speed of a helicopter.

2. Fatigue

No, not the pilot getting tired, but fatigue in the dynamic components. As speed increases, both the forces acting on components and vibration level, increase. This causes fatigue and an increased risk of failure of the components. Of course, you could beef up the components, but this would mean an increase in weight. The components are designed to be a compromise between weight, speed of the helicopter and fatigue life.

3. Power Available

As we saw in the chapter eight, in level flight there comes a time when there is no more power available to overcome any further increase in total drag. This is the maximum level flight speed.

4. Airflow Reversal

A blade is designed so that air goes over it from the leading to the trailing edge :

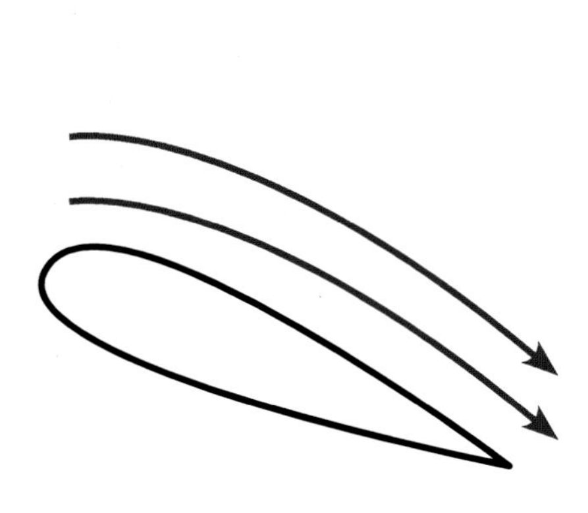

This is what generates lift. Even on the retreating side of the disc, when the air the helicopter is flying into is coming from behind the blade, the speed of the blade relative to this effective wind means that the air is still going over the blade from the leading edge to the trailing edge.

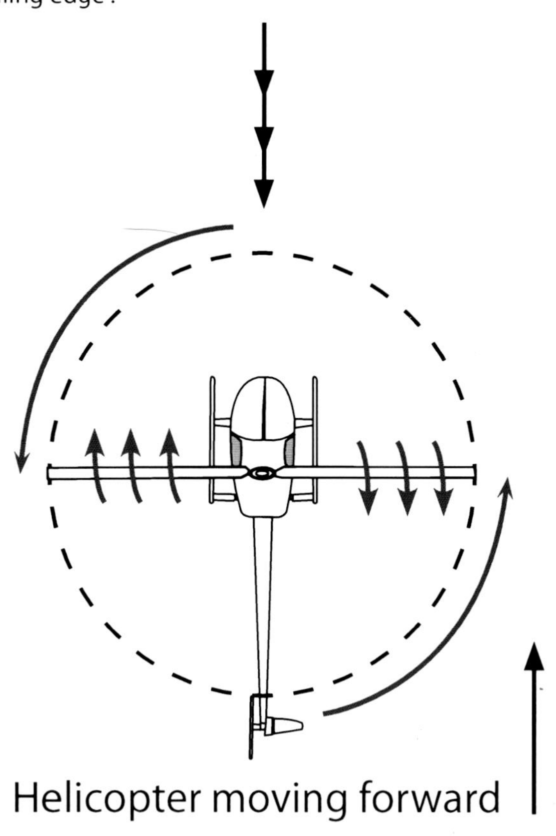

However, if the helicopter goes very fast this is no longer the case. The airflow is reversed and the air travels from the trailing edge to the leading edge, which, of course, is not conducive to the generation of lift.

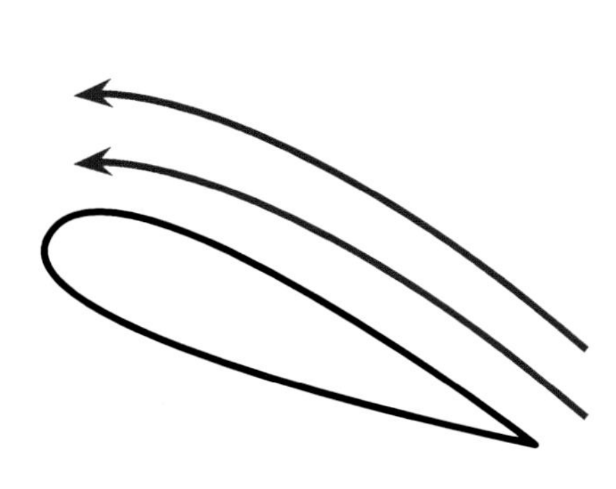

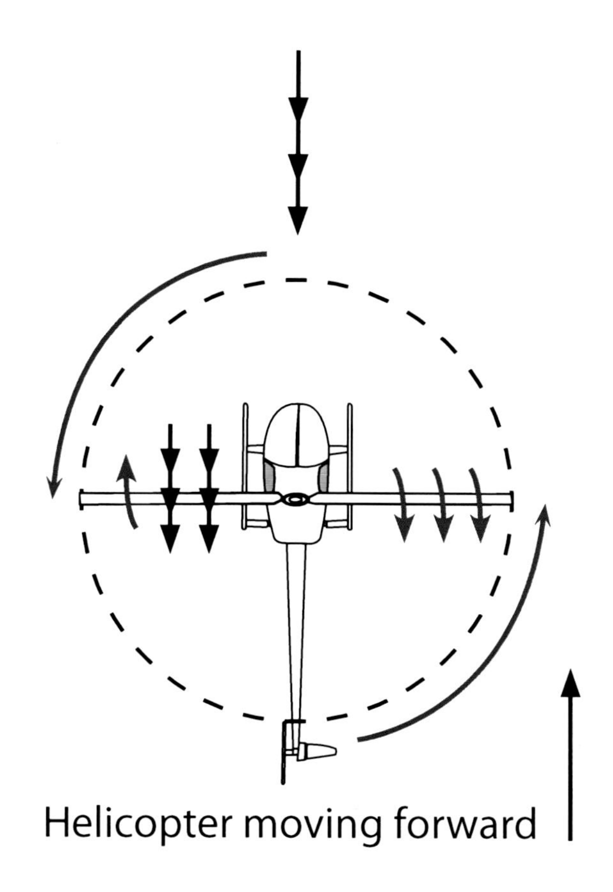

This takes place around the area where most of the effective wind is behind the blade (90° on the retreating side) and where the rotational speed of the blade is the slowest (near the root area).

5. Retreating Blade Stall

If you recall or refer back to the explanation of Flapping to Equality, you will note that the advancing blade is flapping upwards. This increases the induced flow. The retreating blade is flapping down. This creates a flow from beneath the blade which reduces the induced flow.

The faster we go the faster the flapping. On the advancing side the increased induced flow doesn't worry us. However on the retreating side the rate of flapping creates an increasing flow that is not only reducing the induced flow but which, by so doing, increases the angle of attack.

Eventually, due to this, the blade reaches its critical angle of attack (most blades stall at approximately 15° to 17° angle of attack) and it stalls.

This effect occurs where the rate of flapping down is greatest, which is approximately 90° on the retreating side, and where the angular movement of the blade in the vertical plane is greatest, which is near the tip.

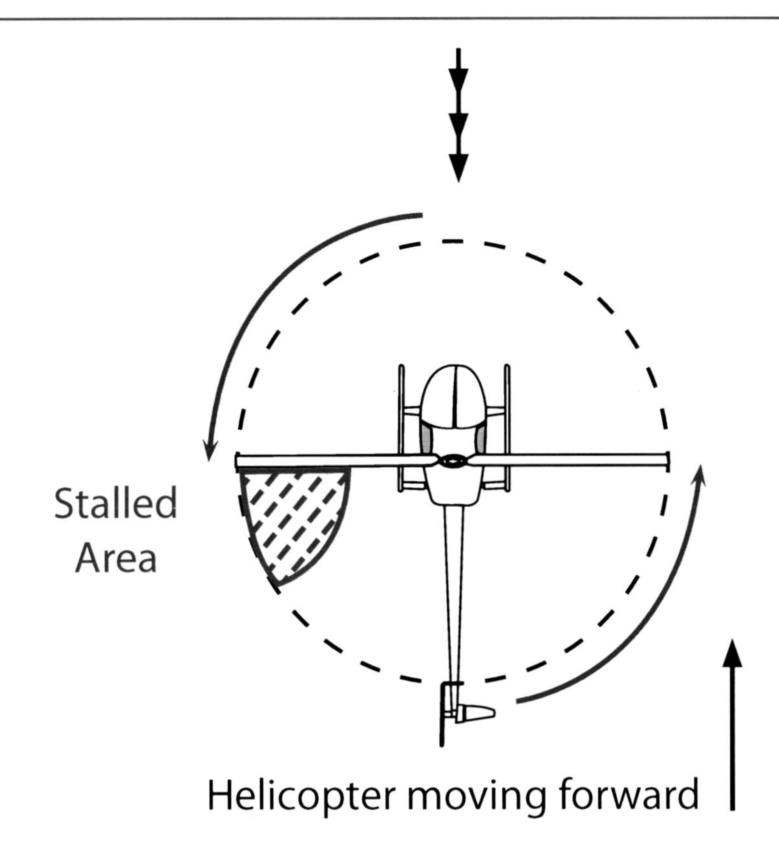

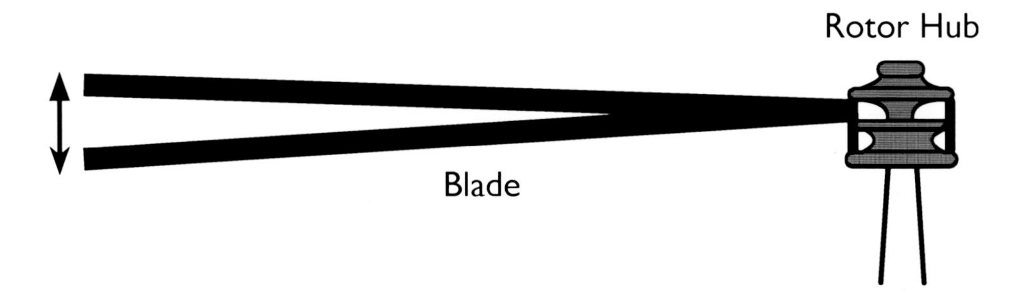

Given a loss of lift in this area the helicopter will pitch nose up and roll to the left. If the pilot tries to correct this with forward and right cyclic, he / she will increase the pitch angle at this critical part and stall the blade further! Correct recovery action is to pitch nose up and roll left (i.e. with the stall) and reduce collective pitch at the same time.

Or, as with many things, the best thing is not to get into this situation in the first place. So do not exceed the design envelope of the helicopter, and in particular do not exceed Vne (Velocity Never Exceed). The good news is that as the blade rotates and the amount of flapping reduces, the stall will die away, on that blade anyway. It will be replaced by the next blade stalling. It is worth mentioning that this can be triggered by pulling hard at high speed, e.g. to avoid a bird.

6. Compressibility

When an aerofoil goes supersonic funny things happen to the airflow over it, necessitating particular design considerations.

It is very difficult to design an aerofoil which is able to cope with both very low speed flight and supersonic flight, which is why some fixed wing aircraft have moving wings i.e. "swept" for high speed flight and "un-swept" for lower speed flight.

Helicopters need to hover, so we take that advantage and give up the top end speed.

Notes :

Axes of Rotation

An aircraft can rotate about three different axes, with a different name for the movement about each axis :

The axis running vertically through the aircraft's centre of gravity is called the Normal Axis. Movement about this axis, which you will see as the nose going left or right, is called Yawing :

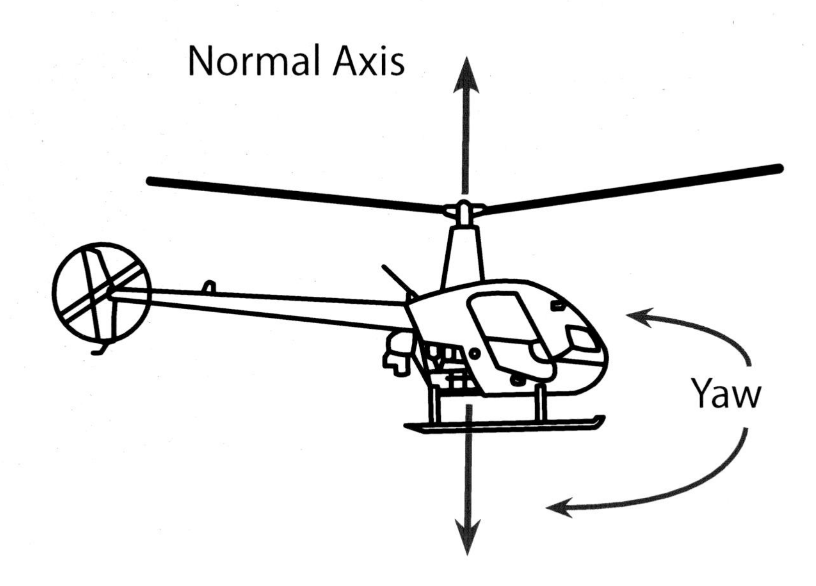

Our next axis runs through the aircraft from the front to the back through the centre of gravity and is called the Longitudinal Axis. Movement about this axis, which you will see as the disc going down to the left and up to the right, or vise versa, is called Rolling :

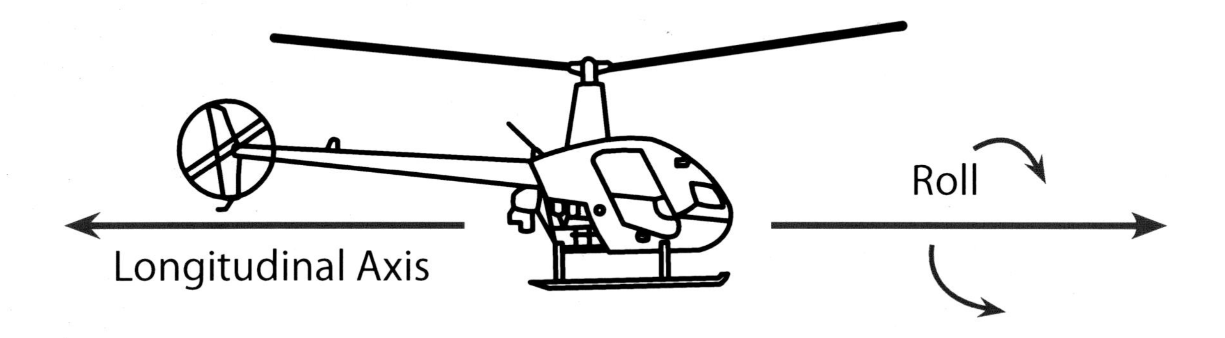

Finally the axis running horizontally through the aircraft's centre of gravity is called the Lateral Axis and movement about this axis, which you will see as the aircraft's nose going up or down, is called Pitching :

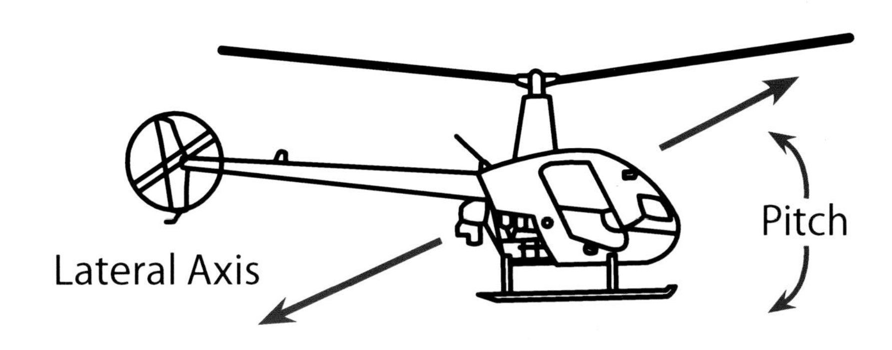

Stability

Stability is what happens to an aircraft after an external force acting upon it (e.g. a gust of wind) is removed. Personally, I find it very difficult to see the stability in the real situation what with wind; convective currents; the head and blades wanging around and a pilot waggling the stick around, often seemingly to little real effect, but nevertheless, here goes :

Static Stability is the immediate reaction once the external force is removed.

Dynamic Stability is the subsequent reaction once the external force is removed.

Each stability, either Static or Dynamic, can itself be one of three kinds :

Positive Stability - STABLE - the aircraft returns to the position it was in prior to the disturbance.

Negative Stability - UNSTABLE - the aircraft continues to depart from its original position.

Neutral Stability - NEUTRAL - the aircraft takes up a new position in constant relation to its original position.

In terms of Static Stability, these can best be understood by taking a cup, a flat sauces and a ball. Put the ball in the bottom of the cup, move it away and let go and it will return from when it was taken - stable. Turn the cup upside down and do the same thing and ball will roll away - unstable. Now do it on the flat saucer (I know - you don't get many saucers that are flat as they wouldn't hold the tea or coffee that you spilt, but please go with the flow) and the ball will stay where you put it - neutral.

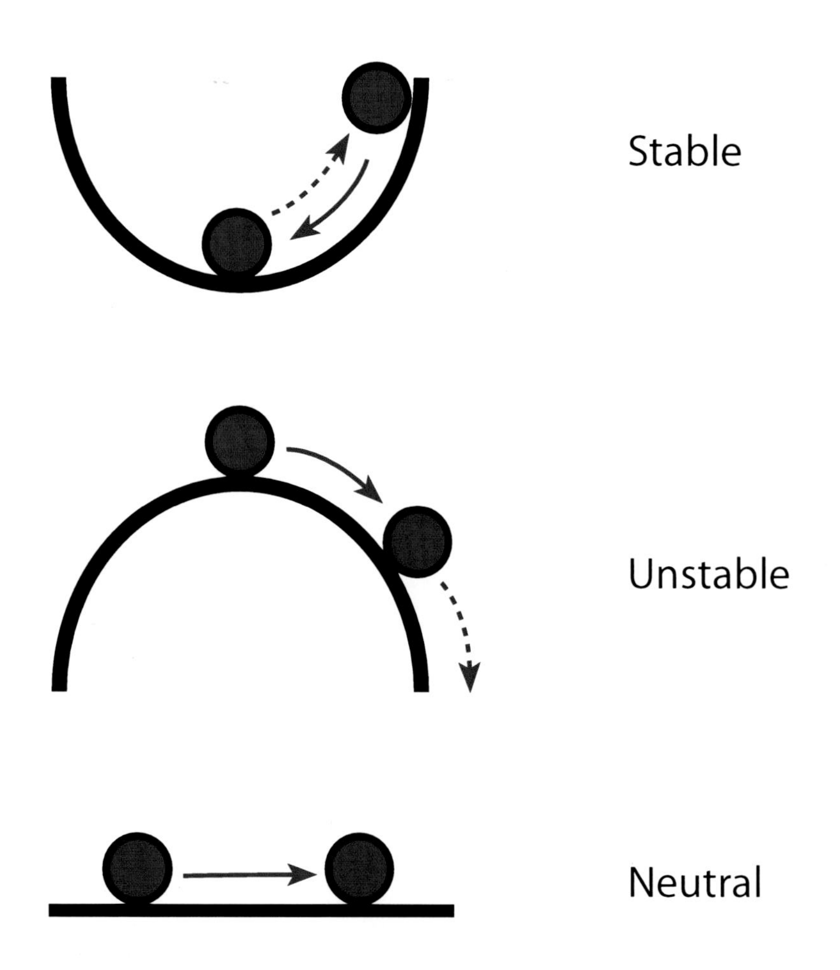

In terms of Dynamic Stability, these can best be understood in terms of a wave activity as per the following diagrams :

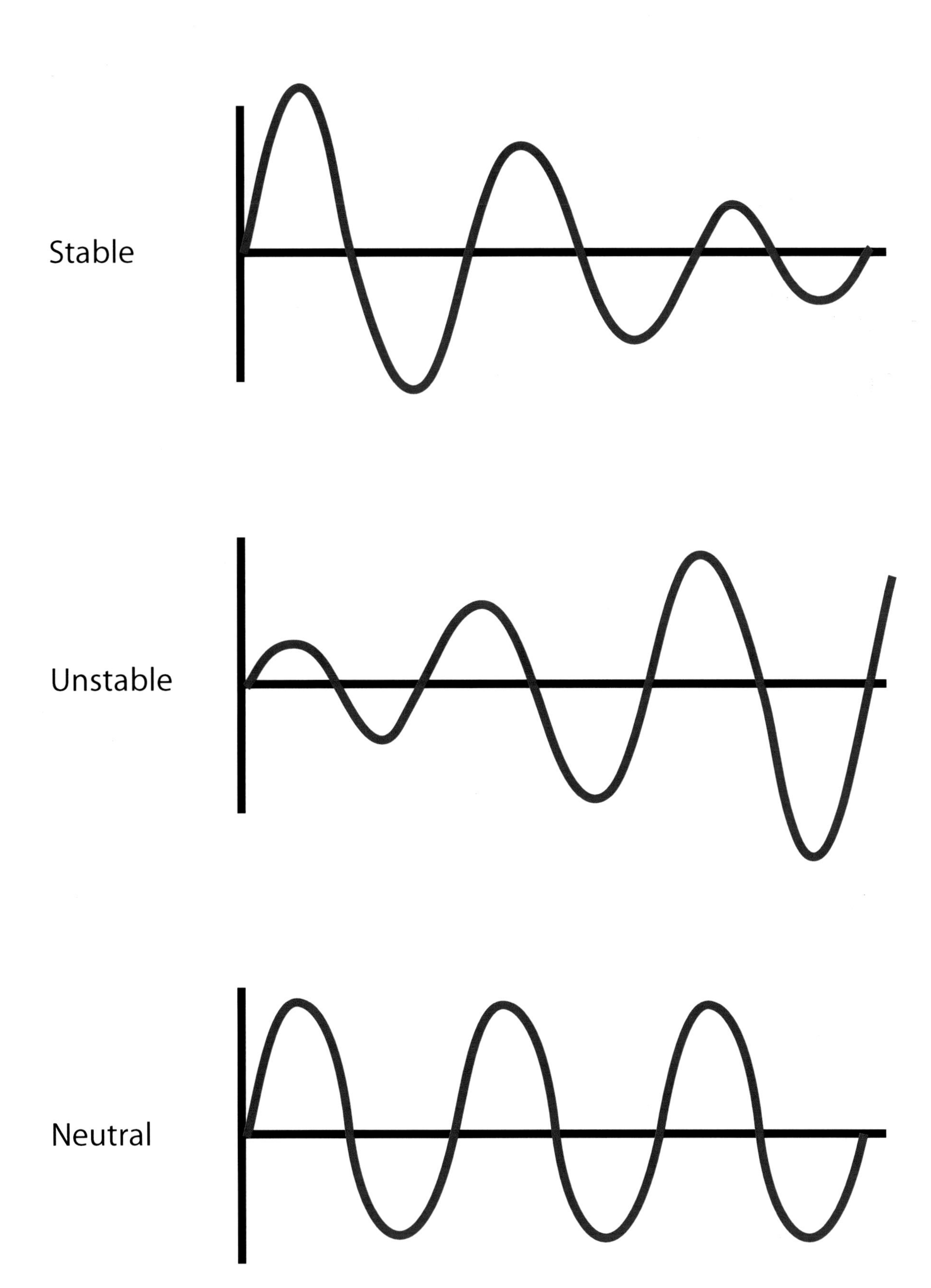

Main Rotor Heads

The rotor head has to be able to accommodate an amazing number of different movements of, and forces acting on, the individual blades. So, for example, a blade during its cycle of rotation will need to flap up, flap down, speed up (lead), slow down (lag), and change its pitch angle - and all at some 500 RPM.

To accomplish this there are three main design "styles"; teetering, fully articulated and semi-rigid. Most two bladed machines have teetering heads whilst three bladed machines generally have fully articulated heads (the three bladed A350, however, has a semi-rigid head - those clever French design chappies!).

The teetering head allows one blade to rise whilst the other falls by way of a teeter hinge. There may also be coning hinges to enable the blades to cone at the same time. To stop the rotor from see-sawing whilst stopping or starting, droop stops may be fitted. Frank Robinson has written some excellent stuff (including an explanation of why he fitted Delta 3 hinges at 18° on the R22) on head design, but this is way too complex for this book. You can track it down on the web if that's your bag.

One problem with the teetering head is that it does leave the helicopter prone to mast bumping if you mishandle it. With mast bumping, the tilt of the rotor disc relative to the mast exceeds the maximum allowed and breaks the mast. This happens because the stability of the system relies on the weight of the helicopter fuselage hanging below the rotor. If the helicopter is put into a negative 'g' situation, either by pilot mishandling (violently pushing the stick forward) or through encountering severe turbulence, the rotor system becomes unloaded. Rotor RPM will decay, rotor thrust is reduced and a roll rate may develop which it may not be possible to control with cyclic. The teeter hinge will damage its stop and may then break the mast. Gulp! If you take a pencil (representing a main rotor mast) and put a plastic cup (representing a main rotor head) upside down on top of it and then tilt the cup so that the edge of it strikes the side of the pencil you will get the general idea. Positive 'g' is a good thing to keep. In fact positive 'g' and Rotor RPM, are two of my favourite companions when flying helicopters. If you do encounter negative 'g', which, of course will only be through turbulence because you now know not to induce it deliberately, apply aft cyclic to reload the disc, and then apply lateral cyclic to control the roll and then pull power.

A fully articulated rotor head allows the blade to move about three hinges : it can flap about a flapping hinge, lead and lag about a dragging hinge, and change pitch about a feathering hinge. This is a great system but has a weight penalty and, of course, is a little more complicated to maintain.

In a semi-rigid rotor head the flapping and dragging hinges are replaced by flexible portions of the blade and hub. Although they are 'flexible' they are more rigid than hinges, hence the name. The semi-rigid head is predominantly used on military designs.

Tail Rotors

The non-shrouded tail rotor is basically a two-bladed teetering head, mounted in the vertical rather than the horizontal plane, but generally without coning hinges. So almost everything we have looked at in relation to the main rotor head, including the vector diagram, applies to the tail rotor, but in a different plane.

A shrouded tail rotor, or 'fenestron', has several more blades rotating in a shroud. It is less vulnerable to damage from foreign objects that the less attentive pilot might try to introduce it to e.g. trees, and has the considerable advantage that stray passers-by cannot walk into it.

The NOTAR (no tail rotor) system does away with the tail rotor altogether and instead uses air under pressure to develop an anti-torque force. This system is also considerably quieter than conventional rotors. On a conventional machine in flight, the majority of the noise is generated by the tail rotor.

Notes :

Notes :